MECHANICS FOR ELECTRICAL AND ELECTRONIC ENGINEERS

MECHANICS FOR ELECTRICAL AND ELECTRONIC ENGINEERS

J. ROGER CALVERT, B.A., Ph.D.
Lecturer in Mechanical Engineering
University of Southampton

ELLIS HORWOOD
NEW YORK   LONDON   TORONTO   SYDNEY   TOKYO   SINGAPORE

First published in 1992 by
ELLIS HORWOOD LIMITED
Market Cross House, Cooper Street,
Chichester, West Sussex, PO19 1EB, England

A division of
Simon & Schuster International Group
A Paramount Communications Company

Printed and bound in Great Britain
by Dotesios, Trowbridge

British Library Cataloguing in Publication Data

A catalogue record for this book is available from the British Library

ISBN 0–13–569922–3   Pbk

Library of Congress Cataloging-in-Publication Data

Available from the publisher

Table of Contents

Preface 9

Part 1: Basic Mechanics

Chapter 1: Introduction 13
Engineering and Mechanics, Modelling, Dimensions, Theory and
Experiment, When Theory Fails, Frames of Reference, Degrees of
Freedom, Free Body Diagrams.

Chapter 2: Fundamental Laws 25
Equilibrium, Newton's Laws, Inertia Forces.

Chapter 3: Statics 33
Boundary and Body Forces, Equilibrium under Gravity, Structures,
Frameworks.

Chapter 4: Kinematics 47
Constant Acceleration, Motion in a Circle, Variable Acceleration

6

Chapter 5: Simple Harmonic Motion 55
    Free Vibration, Forced Vibration and Resonance

Chapter 6: Work and energy 71
    Conservation of Energy, Work, Power, Conservative and Non-
    conservative Forces, Damped Free Vibration, Damped Forced Vibration

Chapter 7: Momentum 91
    Conservation and Change of Momentum, Rebound.

Chapter 8: Angular motion 101
    Definitions, Motion of a Particle about a Point, Solid Bodies, Moment
    of Inertia, Effects of gearing, Simultaneous Rotational and Linear
    Motion.

Part 2: Basic Stress/Strain 119

Chapter 9: Introduction 121
    Stress and Strain, Elastic Materials, Shear, Calculation of Stresses,
    Strains and Extensions, Pressure Vessels.

Chapter 10: Bending 133
    Shear Force and Bending Moment, Macaulay's Notation, Superposition,
    Bending Stresses and Strains, Shear Stress, Deflection under Bending,
    Design of Beams, Combined End Load and Bending.

Chapter 11: Torsion 153
    Torque Diagrams, Shear Stress and Strain in Circular Shafts, Torsion
    of a Tube, The Coil Spring, Non-uniform Shafts.

Chapter 12: Material Properties 165
    Tensile Testing, Compression, Torsion, Hardness.

Chapter 13: Failure and its Avoidance 171
    What is Failure?, Modes of Structural Failure, Safety Factors.

Appendices

I Moments of inertia 181

II Second moments of area 185

III Beam Bending Formulae 191

IV Material Properties 195

Index 197

Preface

The intention of this book is to cover the rudiments of mechanics for a professional engineer or scientist for whom it is not a specialist subject. It is equivalent to a one unit course (about 25 lectures and associated tutorial work). It assumes a mathematical background covering simple integration and differentiation and some acquaintance with vectors.

It sets out to answer two main questions: (1) what falls within the scope of mechanics, what problems may arise within it and what problems may be solved within it? (2) what kind of problems in this subject can I solve myself, and how do I know when I should call in a specialist?

Within these two areas, the book is complete. It does not, however, include many of the details which a traditional mechanics textbook (for specialists) would include, and does not always give rigorous derivations of the results presented. The reasons for this restriction are two-fold: (1) to avoid obscuring the principles with detail; (2) to keep down the size and cost. For those requiring, or interested in, more depth, a bibliography of more complete works is provided at the end of each chapter in Part 1 and at the end of Chapter 9, covering the whole of Part 2.

The book is primarily aimed at first year university students of Electrical and Electronic Engineering, and many of the examples are biased towards applications in the electrical field. However, the general principles and approach should be equally applicable to students of other engineering and scientific specialities whose main field is not mechanics.

The book is divided into two main sections: Basic Mechanics (incorporating statics, kinematics and dynamics of linear and rotating systems) and Basic Stress/Strain (incorporating elasticity, bending and torsion). Appendices give numerical and reference data. Each chapter ends with examples for student use.

Numerical answers are given; more detailed solutions are available from the author.

Southampton   J Roger Calvert
June 1992

Part 1
Basic Mechanics

1

Introduction

In this chapter, we will look at the fundamental ideas underlying all of science and engineering, and at how they apply to the sub-discipline of mechanics.

1.1 ENGINEERING AND MECHANICS

Engineering is all about controlling things. It is the job of the engineer to make things happen which would not otherwise take place, or to prevent things from happening which would do. The things controlled are part of the physical world - they may be tangible objects made out of solid, liquid or gaseous materials, intangible (but none the less real) phenomena such as heat or electricity, or abstract quantities such as information (although the latter have to be put into a physical form such as electrical impulses or sound waves before they can be put to practical use).

In order to control things, we need to understand their behaviour both in the undisturbed state and when we are attempting to influence them. Unless we can predict what will happen naturally, we do not know if we want to change it. Unless we can predict what the effects of our change will be, we are unlikely to achieve the desired result.

Engineering is traditionally divided vertically into sub-professions according to the application involved - Civil, Mechanical, Electrical and many others. Inevitably, the fields of interest of these overlap in many ways. It is also divided horizontally into subjects according to the type of object which is being controlled - solid, fluid, thermal, electrical, information, and so on. Most of these subjects are of interest to more than one of the sub-professions, and a professional engineer will generally be a specialist in a particular group of subjects and have a working awareness of many others.

Mechanics is the study of force and motion, and the relationships between them. It is one of the oldest branches of engineering - there has always been a need to move things or stop them. It is also one of the oldest branches of applied mathematics; our modern mechanics is the work of a long succession of people from Archimedes (287 - 212 BC), through to Galileo (1564 - 1642) and Newton (1642 - 1727). The system of mechanics founded by Newton and developed by many later workers is known as classical mechanics, and is perfectly adequate for nearly all engineering applications. In extreme cases such as very small or very high speed situations, it is inadequate, and other systems of mechanics (quantum and relativistic, respectively) have been developed. This book is entirely confined to Newtonian mechanics.

As applied to solid bodies and materials, mechanics is of interest to virtually all engineers. Nearly everything involves solid objects which are required to be moved, or to be prevented from moving. For many mechanical engineers, mechanics is the central subject. For most other engineers of all specialities it intervenes frequently. Very often the level of understanding required is within their experience. In occasional cases, they may need to call in specialist help in solving their problems. It is important to be able to decide when this is necessary.

Four branches of mechanics concern us here. *Statics* is the study of forces alone. This is covered in Chapter III. *Kinematics* is the study of motion alone; it is the subject of Chapter IV. *Dynamics* is the study of the interaction between forces and motion, and occupies the rest of Part 1. *Solid Mechanics* brings in the properties of solid materials, and makes up Part 2. We will not concern ourselves with the mechanics of fluids, soils, powders or other types of material, though these are of great interest to particular specialists.

1.2 MODELLING

It is rarely possible to make sufficient observations of naturally occurring phenomena to be able to predict their behaviour adequately (although in some scientific disciplines such as astronomy few alternatives are available). Usually, understanding is gained by making known changes to the physical world, and observing the outcome. This is experimentation, and is by and large the preserve of the scientist - the engineer will make use of the understanding that the scientist has obtained to control the physical world. Very often the same individual will spend some time acquiring understanding - science - and some time using it - engineering.

The small portion of the physical world used to predict the future behaviour of another part of it is a model. In this case it is a physical and direct model. However, in many cases, analogies may be drawn between two different types of phenomena, and an indirect model can be used. For example, in some situations the flow of heat through a thermal conductor behaves in a similar manner to the flow of electric current through an electrical conductor. One can be used as an indirect model of the other.

In many situations in the physical sciences, it is found that if various quantities in the real world are associated with terms in a mathematical equation, the world and the equation behave in a similar manner. The equation is an indirect model of the real world: a mathematical model. By doing experiments on the model (i.e. solving the equations), we can predict what will happen in the real situation. Such experiments (calculations) are usually considerably simpler, cheaper and faster than the equivalent physical experiments, and are therefore usually used in preference wherever possible.

Often, there is more than one model available to describe a given problem. Then we should choose the simplest one which adequately does the job. For example, the use of relativistic mechanics instead of Newtonian mechanics in calculating the flight time of a supersonic transatlantic aircraft could lead to an improved estimate of arrival time by about 25 ns (in which time the aircraft travels about 20 μm). This is trivial, and is not worth the extra effort involved. More down to earth, in calculating the performance of an electric milk float, we might be able to neglect the effects of air resistance. But in calculating the motion of a 300 km h^{-1} electric train, we clearly cannot. The fundamental principles and even the calculation methods are the same for both, but the dominant terms in the equations are different. This principle of choosing the simplest theory consistent with the data is called *Ockham's razor*, after William of Ockham (1285 - 1349) who had similar thoughts.

1.3 DIMENSIONS

When a term in a mathematical equation is associated with a physical quantity, it acquires an extra property called its *dimension*. This is the quality which distinguishes different types of physical quantities. We all know that lengths and masses are different. It is perfectly valid to add 1 m to 2.5 m (or even, with suitable unit conversions, 1 km to 2.5 miles), but it can never be valid to add 1 m to 2.5 kg.

This places restrictions on the forms that the equations in mathematical models can take. All the terms in any equation which are added, subtracted or equated must have the same dimensions.

This simple concept is in fact very powerful. It is the basis of an extremely general theory known as *Dimensional Analysis*. This can be used to explore the shapes mathematical models must have, and to show relationships between apparently diverse problems. Dimensional analysis is widely used in fluid mechanics, where more detailed mathematical models are sparse. Many examples appear in the references.

Dimensions are closely related to *units*, which are simply an example of a quantity with the appropriate dimensions. Quantities with different dimensions must have different units. But as well as being dimensionally correct, equations must also be correct as regards units.

Dimensions and units provide a check on the form of the equations in our mathematical model. If the dimensions do not match, it cannot be a valid model. If the dimensions balance, but not the units, the data must be converted. Unfortunately, even if both units and dimensions balance, there is no guarantee that the theory is valid; we can only say that it is not certainly invalid.

1.4 THEORY AND EXPERIMENT

A mathematical model is sometimes called a theory, and its predictions are called theoretical predictions. But this does not give it a status in any way different from any other model. All theories used by engineers are approximate: there are regions of application where they will give incorrect predictions. The application of a mathematical model must always ultimately depend on experimental verification. Whether there is (or should be) an "exact theory of everything" is a matter for physicists (and philosophers), not engineers. But there is no doubt that many small parts of the real world can be described very well indeed by fairly simple mathematical models. It is the engineer's job to select an appropriate model of a particular system, and use it to predict the system's behaviour.

Sometimes, we may not have an accepted model, or one that produces predictions of sufficient accuracy. Then we may have to experiment - that is observe the behaviour of some part of the real world itself. Models become accepted because they agree with experiments, and must be restricted in application or discarded if they do not.

The experiments need not always be carried out on the "original" system. Very general models, such as dimensional analysis, may allow us to carry out physical experiments on one system and use them to predict the behaviour of another.

If on any particular occasion we have predictions from an accepted theoretical model which do not appear to agree with the results of experiment, then it must be the theory which is wrong. The experiment **is** the real world. This does not mean that the theory is useless; it means that we have mis-applied it somehow.

As an example, there are well-established theories for the flow of oil through bearings. In the 1960s, these were used to design the bearings for new 500 MW power station turbo-alternators. The machines did not behave as expected, and it turned out that the large size of the bearings had resulted in the flow becoming turbulent. Turbulent flow behaves in a very different manner from the type of flow (laminar) assumed by the theory. Turbulent flow is well known in many other areas; the designers had just not thought to consider it in the context of bearings. A new theory was needed to handle the problem of turbulent flow in bearings, but the conventional theory, with laminar flow, is still perfectly usable in the situations for which it was developed.

All theories are approximate; they are based on assumptions which should be, but are not always, clearly stated. Failure of an established theory to give correct predictions means that one or more of these assumptions must have been violated.

Possibilities to look for in such cases are: implicit assumptions about the value of some quantity (e.g. g, the acceleration due to gravity or the properties of some material); assumptions that some quantity does not change over the duration of the event considered (e.g. ambient temperature and pressure); variables being taken outside their normal range (as in the example above).

1.5 WHEN THEORY FAILS

It often appears in textbooks and courses that there is a theory for everything. This is far from the truth. It is just that theory is easy to teach, so courses concentrate on situations where it exists.

But some natural phenomena seem to be so complex that there is as yet no firmly established body of theory. Examples are magnetic properties of materials, turbulent fluid flow, structural properties of polymers, etc. All these are areas of mathematical, scientific and engineering research. To predict the behaviour of these systems (as engineers must), we use very general modelling such as dimensional analysis, experiment, what are known as empirical theories (fitting straight lines to scattered experimental data) and most important of all, engineering tradition, experience and judgement.

Some mathematical models (equations) are said to have "no solution". This usually means that mathematicians have been unable to find a solution which can be written in terms of algebraic expressions and relatively simple functions such as logarithm, square root or cosine. Indeed, in many cases mathematicians can prove that no such solution exists. But these functions are usually themselves defined as the solution of some equation which previously had no solution, and numerical methods have been developed for their evaluation. Numerical methods can (with modern computer power) solve many equations which have no "explicit" solution. There is no real difference between "analytic" and "numerical" solutions of equations, and the latter will play an increasingly important role in engineering theory as computer techniques evolve.

1.6 FRAMES OF REFERENCE

The study of motion requires a *frame of reference*. The only way we can determine the velocity of something is by watching it go past something else. The velocities are *relative*, and we cannot say which of the two objects is moving and which is stationary. To determine a velocity, we need a co-ordinate system which defines three distinct directions (since velocity is a vector) and is assumed to be stationary. Such a co-ordinate system is called a frame of reference. The three directions defined are usually, though not necessarily, perpendicular to each other. Various co-ordinate systems are used according to the symmetries of the problem under investigation; the most common are the Cartesian and the cylindrical polar systems. Conversion of co-ordinates from one of these systems to the other is straightforward.

As we will see in Chapter II, one of the consequences of Newton's laws of motion is that it does not matter if the frame of reference is moving at constant velocity, or is truly stationary. In fact, we have no way of finding out which is the case and the term "truly stationary" has no meaning. A frame of reference which is moving at constant velocity (or stationary) is called an *inertial* frame. We can easily convert velocities in one inertial frame to another by subtracting the (vector) relative velocity of the second frame from all the velocities in the first frame.

On the other hand, it *does* matter if the frame of reference is accelerating (*non-inertial*). Acceleration is an absolute quantity, and we can detect whether or not we are accelerating. If you are sitting in a railway carriage you may find it hard to tell if you are moving one way or the train in the next platform is moving the other way. But should one of the two trains hit the buffers, it would be immediately obvious which one had undergone the acceleration. Standing passengers would fall over in one, but not in the other.

Motion in a circle involves acceleration towards the centre of the circle (see Chapter 4), so that a rotating frame of reference is non-inertial. If you move radially on a roundabout in a children's playground, you get forced against the rails. The radial direction is changing with time, the frame of reference is rotating. You cannot bring a rotating system to rest (from the dynamic point of view) by superimposing a rotation in the opposite sense. It **is** quite possible to convert between rotating and non-rotating frames of reference, but the form of the equations of motion changes. This is the origin of the fictitious centrifugal and Coriolis forces. They are just terms which appear in the equations of motion in a rotating frame of reference, but not in an inertial one (this point will be discussed further in Chapter 2).

1.7 DEGREES OF FREEDOM

To define the position of a point in three-dimensional space requires three co-ordinate values. Anything other than a point requires more. For example, a line of known length requires five - three to locate one end, then two more for the other (the line length provides the third for the other end). A plane shape (e.g. a triangle) needs six - five for one of its edges (a line), and another to represent rotation about that edge. This is also the number needed for a solid body.

The number of values which are needed to define the position of an object is called the number of *degrees of freedom* of the object. For a rigid body, it is never more than six. A body which can deform or a mechanism made of elements hinged together may require many more. On the other hand, many of the mathematical models we use are simplified to two or even one dimension, and have many fewer degrees of freedom. Figure 1.1 is an illustration of this: only one value is needed to define the position of a vehicle along a road between two points. If the vehicle is towing a kite on a line of known length (Figure 1.2), however, two are needed.

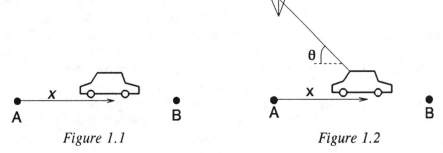

Figure 1.1   Figure 1.2

To prevent a body moving, we must apply as many *constraints* as it has degrees of freedom; any less, and some part of it will be able to move.

1.8 FREE BODY DIAGRAMS

When applying laws of motion to real objects, it is important to be clear as to precisely what objects and what forces we are considering. Real systems usually have several components which interact with each other. In every such case, pairs of equal and opposite forces will exist (by Newton's third law - see Chapter 2). Unless we are very careful, we can easily associate the wrong one of the pair with the body, and so end up with an incorrect sign.

A notation which helps us to keep control of such things is the *Free Body Diagram*. We first decide which parts of our system we wish to consider separately. These might be groups of objects, single objects or even parts of objects. We then draw a separate diagram for each of them, and on that diagram show only that part and the forces which act **on** it from elsewhere. We do not show forces which the object exerts on anything else, nor forces which are internal to the object.

As an example, let us again consider our car towing a kite, shown in the *system* diagram in Figure 1.3:

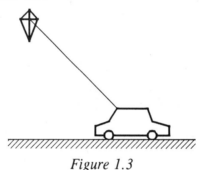

Figure 1.3

The free body diagram for the whole thing is shown in Figure 1.4, where **W** is the total weight of the car (and kite), **H** and **V** are the horizontal and vertical components of the force applied to the car by the road, and **D** and **L** those applied to the kite by the air[*]. Note that the road itself does not appear in this diagram, since it is not part of the item we are considering. Neither does the tension in the string, since this is internal to the item.

If we wish to separate the car and the kite, we get the two free body diagrams in Figure 1.5. The string tension **T** is now an external force, and appears in both diagrams, in opposite directions. (These could, of course, be further split into horizontal and vertical components).

We could take this further - for example, we might wish to consider the forces on one wheel of the car. The car free body diagram would then split into

---

[*] No real attempt has been made here to show the lines of action of the forces realistically. This would be important in cases where moments (discussed in Chapter 2 were being taken to study rotational motion (or equilibrium).

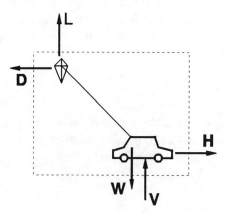

Figure 1.4

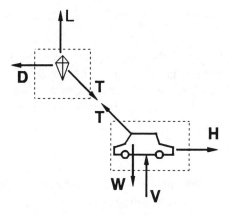

Figure 1.5

two parts (one for the wheel and one for the rest of the car), and a matched pair of forces appear between the two. The forces **V** and **H** would also have to be split, since they partly act through this wheel and partly through the others.

Incidentally, we notice that the forces in the diagrams are not necessarily balanced. If they are not, the various bodies will accelerate, but this is a matter for the equations of motion; the free body diagrams are independent of it.

In a similar way, we must be clear as to the sign convention for positions of objects and directions of forces, velocities and accelerations. If we use more than one origin or positive direction, we must clearly relate them to each other, or chaos will ensue. Usually, a free body diagram will include some indication of the origins and positive directions chosen for the various distances and forces (as used for the co-ordinate x, in Figure 1.1). Velocities and accelerations will use the same directions as the distances. We will see many examples of this elsewhere in the book.

EXAMPLES

1.1   In the following formulae, V stands for velocity, L and x for lengths, g for the acceleration due to gravity (units m s^{-2}) and t for time. Which of them are dimensionally consistent?

(i) $V = 2\sqrt{(gL)}$
(ii) $L = 1.2\sqrt{(x)}$
(iii) $t = L/g$
(iv) $t = 2\pi\sqrt{(L/g)}$
(v) $x = L + gt^2$
(vi) $x = L + 2gt$
(vii) $x = L + 1$

(Ans: i, iv, v)

1.2   The outer diameter of the playing surface of an LP record is 300 mm, the inner diameter is 100 mm. The pitch of the groove spiral is 0.15 mm. Assuming the stylus moves in a straight line, sketch its path and estimate how far it travels relative to (a) the record, and (b) a fixed frame of reference. Which of these distances is relevant to (i) the playing time of the record, and (ii) the life of the stylus?
(Ans: 419 m, 0.1 m)

1.3   Which of the following frames of reference are inertial (ignoring any effects due to the motion of the earth)?

(a) Relative to the inside of a vehicle travelling uphill at constant speed;

(b) Relative to the inside of a vehicle under normal driving conditions;

(c) Relative to a parachutist falling at a steady rate;

(d) Relative to a moving lift, which still has some way to go before its next stop;

(e) Relative to the jib of a tower crane, which is rotating about a vertical axis;

(f) Relative to a moving escalator.

(Ans: a, c, d, f)

1.4   How many degrees of freedom have the following systems?
   (a) a joystick;
   (b) the hook on a factory gantry crane;
   (c) the door on a lift;
   (d) a car accelerator;
   (e) a light switch;
   (f) the bucket on a tractor mounted digger;
   (g) the bulb of a desk lamp.
 (Ans: 2, 3, 2, 1, 1, 4, 5)

1.5   Draw free body diagrams appropriate for analysing the equilibrium or motion of (a) the rotor of a motor car alternator, (b) the clapper of an electric bell, (c) a car jack, (d) a disabled person's stair lift.

BIBLIOGRAPHY

Basics:

Collinson CD, *Introductory Mechanics*. Edward Arnold, 1980 (Chapter 1)
Synge JL and Griffith BA, *Principles of Mechanics*. McGraw-Hill 1959 (Chapter 1)

Dimensional Analysis:

Douglas JF, Gasiorek JM and Swaffield JA, *Fluid Mechanics*. 2nd edition, Pitman 1985 (Chapter VII)

Numerical data and formulae for all parts of the book:

Munday AJ and Farrar RA, *An Engineering Data Book*. Macmillan 1979.

2

Fundamental Laws

In this chapter we introduce the basic mathematical models on which the whole of classical mechanics depends. Some of these laws virtually have the status of axioms or definitions, while some are more explicitly based on experiment.

2.1 EQUILIBRIUM

If all the external forces acting on a body sum to zero, the body is said to be *in equilibrium*. It follows from the laws of motion (see below) that it then cannot be accelerating; it must either be at rest or be moving at constant velocity. In the latter case we can, as discussed in Chapter 1, define an inertial frame of reference in which the body is stationary, and the problem is one of statics.

The converse also applies: if a body is found to be at rest or moving at constant velocity in some inertial frame of reference, any external forces acting on it must sum to zero.

Forces are vectors, having both magnitude and direction. But they also have a specific line of action, and the conditions for equilibrium must include consideration of this. For example, in Figure 2.1a, the two forces are co-linear, and sum to zero. In Figure 2.1b, they are parallel, but not co-linear. They tend to produce a rotation of the body.

The amount of rotative tendency is called the *moment* of the force. This is defined as the product of the magnitude of the force and the perpendicular

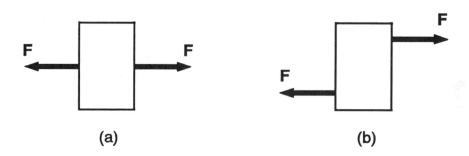

Figure 2.1

distance between the line of action of the force and some specified point. (In a three dimensional situation, the moment must be relative to an axis, not a point, and is most easily defined in terms of vector products. We will not be considering such situations in this book.)

The moment of a force about various points will generally depend on the positions of the points. In particular, a force has no moment about any point on its line of action. However, for bodies in equilibrium, the sum of the moments of all the external forces about any specified point will be zero.

The conditions which must be satisfied for a body to be in equilibrium under a set of forces are thus:

- the magnitudes of the forces sum (vectorially) to zero, and
- the sum of the moments of the forces about any axis is also zero.

In a one-dimensional situation, there is only one component of force, and no moment. In two dimensions, there are two components of force and one of moment. In three dimensions there are three of each. In fact, the number of conditions which must be satisfied for equilibrium is the same as the number of degrees of freedom of the body.

Bodies in equilibrium are considered further in Chapter 3.

2.2 NEWTON'S LAWS

The whole of engineering mechanics (sometimes known as "classical mechanics" to distinguish it from other mathematical models which are of interest to physicists) is based on Newton's three laws of motion. These taken together form a mathematical model which very successfully describes the motion of massive bodies (i.e. bodies with mass - not necessarily large or heavy bodies).

The modern statement of these laws is rather different from Newton's original statement; he was, of course, having to develop the terminology as he went along. Experience in applying the laws over the last three hundred years, and standardisation of terminology, has produced more precise and concise statements of them.

The laws of motion have very fundamental status. In many respects, they might be considered to be definitions rather than assumptions.

We will only consider the forms that the laws take in an inertial frame of reference. Although the surface of the earth is not an inertial frame of reference, it may often be treated as such to a satisfactory degree of accuracy. Contrary to their numbering, we will consider the third law first, as it is more fundamental than the others.

2.2.1 Newton's third law

This law states that all forces come in pairs. If a body 'A' exerts a force **F** on another body 'B', then body 'B' will exert a (co-linear) force **-F** on body 'A': "To every action there is an equal and opposite reaction". The forces can arise from any source - mechanical, electrical, magnetic, etc. They can be contact forces (external loads), internal forces (stresses), body forces (arising from magnetic or gravitational fields), etc. The law does not imply equilibrium of the bodies between which the forces act. According to what other forces are present, either 'A' or 'B' or both may accelerate as predicted by Newton's second law.

2.2.2 Newton's first and second laws of motion

There is no real need to separate these two; the first law states that if no force is applied to a body, its acceleration will be zero, while the second law states that if a (vector) force is applied, the (vector) acceleration which results is proportional to and in the same direction as the force.

In symbols,

$$\mathbf{F} = kM\mathbf{a}$$

where **F** is the force applied to the body, M is its mass and **a** is the acceleration. k is a constant which depends on the system of units.

In the SI system of units*, this equation defines the unit of force. With the mass in kilogrammes (kg), distances in metres (m) and time in seconds (s), the acceleration will be in m s^{-2} and the force newtons (N). The constant k is dimensionless and identically equal to 1. Some other systems of units have a non-unit value of k.

2.2.3 Newton's law of gravitation

Often associated with the three laws of motion is Newton's law of gravitation. This is, however, a much less fundamental law. Gravitation, as described by this law, was the first *field* to be discovered, followed later by electrical, magnetic and other fields. It is heavily based on experiment, and although quite adequate for virtually all engineering applications, has shortcomings on cosmological scales. There are many proposed alternative theories of gravitation - Einstein's general theory of relativity is one of the better known and more successful.

The law of gravitation states that a force of attraction exists between two massive bodies given by:

$$F = G\frac{M_1 M_2}{R^2}$$

where M_1 and M_2 are the masses of the bodies, and R is the distance between their centres of mass. G is an experimental constant which, in SI units, has a value of about 6.67×10^{-11} N m^2 kg^{-2}. The force is one of attraction, directed along the line joining the centres of mass of the two bodies. (Centre of mass will be defined in Chapter 3)

In very many applications, one of the masses is that of the earth (about 6×10^{24} kg), and the distance between the masses is approximately equal to the radius of the earth (about 6400 km). The law can then be simplified to

$$F = Mg$$

where M is the mass we are concerned with, and g (which has the same dimensions as acceleration) is called the *acceleration due to gravity*. In such cases, F is known as the *weight* of the body. Because of non-uniformities in the structure of the earth, the value of g varies significantly from place to place on

---

* The Système International d'Unités, an internationally standardised system of units covering the whole of science and engineering in a consistent and rational manner.

the surface of the earth, and even more so off the surface (in space or on the moon). For reference purposes, a standard value of about 9.81 m s^{-2} is used.

2.3 INERTIA FORCES

Consider a body in equilibrium under the action of two forces F_1 and F_2: the equation of equilibrium is

$$F_1 + F_2 = 0$$

Now consider the same body (which is of mass M) acted on by the force F_1 alone: the equation relating force to acceleration (the *equation of motion*) is

$$F_1 = Ma \qquad \text{or} \qquad F_1 - Ma = 0$$

Comparison of the two shows that (algebraically), the mass-acceleration term in the last equation may be replaced by a force term of the same magnitude, but opposite sign. This appears to transform the dynamic equation of motion into a static equilibrium equation, which might be easier to visualize.

The force introduced is called an *inertia* or *d'Alembert* force (after the mathematician who proposed this substitution). It is completely fictitious, being simply a change in notation. The use of such methods may appear to simplify some calculations, but unless the user is absolutely clear of their origin and status, serious misunderstandings and errors can result.

Centrifugal force is an example of an inertia force. A body travelling around a circular path of radius r at constant speed v is subject to an acceleration v^2/r towards the centre of the path (see Chapter 4). This arises simply from the geometry of the system. The equation of motion is

$$F = M\frac{v^2}{r} \qquad \text{or} \qquad F + F_c = 0$$

$$\text{where} \quad F_c = -M\frac{v^2}{r}$$

F_c is the so-called centrifugal force, directed outwards. F is the centripetal force, directed inwards. This latter *does* exist - it must, otherwise the body could not travel round its circle. It may have many physical forms - magnetic, gravitational, reaction force from a track, tension in a string, etc - but it must be there.

In a rotating (and therefore non-inertial) co-ordinate system, the introduction of centrifugal force into the equations avoids an apparently arbitrary acceleration appearing. Another such inertia force/acceleration pair is also needed when there is radial motion in a rotating coordinate system - the so-called Coriolis effect.

In relativity theory, weight is also shown to be an inertia force. An appropriate choice of frame of reference (using more than three dimensions) avoids the necessity of a separate experimental theory of gravitation.

This discussion of inertia forces is presented for clarification only. The reader is not encouraged to make use of them in any circumstances. Accelerating (dynamic) systems should be treated as such, and not made to appear like static systems.

EXAMPLES

2.1   Which of the following situations are in equilibrium:
(a) A vehicle driving up a hill at constant speed;
(b) A vehicle driving round a roundabout at constant speed;
(c) A ski jumper before take-off;
(d) A ski jumper after take-off;
(e) An aircraft flying at constant speed and rate of descent;
(f) An aircraft at the moment of take-off?
(Ans: a and e)

2.2   A 60 kg woman stands on a spring operated weighing machine in a lift. The machine shows 75 kg. What is the acceleration of the lift?
(Ans: 2.45 m s^{-2})

2.3   A lift of mass 1 tonne attains a velocity of 6 m s^{-1} in 3 m. Assuming constant acceleration, calculate the tension in the lift cable.
(Ans: 15.8 kN)

2.4   A train of mass 500 tonnes is propelled by an electromagnetic device which produces a force of 1.5 MN over the first 50 m of each kilometre of track, and is subject to a resisting force of 75 kN. Show that the train arrives at the end of the first kilometre going at the same speed as it started. For an initial speed of 80 km h^{-1}, calculate (a) the maximum speed reached, and (b) the average speed over the kilometre.
(Ans: 100.5 km h^{-1}, 90.25 km h^{-1})

2.5   By considering the equation of motion of the earth, estimate the mass of the sun. (The radius of the earth's orbit is approximately 1.5×10^8 km.)
(Ans: 2×10^{30} kg)

2.6   Saturn is about 10 times the diameter and 100 times the mass of the earth. Estimate the weight of a pint of beer on Saturn, ignoring effects due to planetary rotation.
(Ans: $0.57g$ N)

2.7   A mass of 1 kg is weighed on a spring balance at the North Pole and at the equator. Approximately what difference of weight would be expected? (The earth is approximately 6400 km radius.)
(Ans: 0.034 N lighter on the equator)

BIBLIOGRAPHY

Equilibrium:

Meriam JL, *Statics*. Wiley 1980

Newton's Laws:

Higginson GR, *Foundations of Engineering Mechanics*. Longman, 1974 (Chapter 3)

Units:

The Use of SI units. British Standards Institution, 1972

3

Statics

Statics is the study of bodies in equilibrium under some appropriate set of forces. The conditions needed for equilibrium have been considered in Chapter 2; here we will look at the calculation of forces for some particular situations.

3.1 BOUNDARY AND BODY FORCES

It is useful to consider two different types of forces which may be applied to a body: boundary forces and body forces.

Boundary forces are forces applied to a body at some particular point (or distributed over an area) on its surface. Examples are the forces applied to the tyres of a road vehicle by the road surface or the force applied by the gripper of a robot to its load. Boundary forces may often be considered as acting at a point (although this is impossible in reality). Sometimes, however, we must take account of their distribution across a finite surface.

Body forces are forces which are applied to the bulk of the material of a body. The most universal is gravity (weight), which acts on every particle in the body. Another body force is the magnetic force, for example the force applied to the armature of a solenoid by the magnetic field generated by the current in the coil.

3.1.1 Centre of mass and centroid

It is usually possible (in statics) to treat body forces as being a single force acting at a single point. In the case of gravity, the force would be the total body weight and the point of action would be the *Centre of Gravity*. In all normal situations, the centre of gravity is at the same place as the *Centre of Mass*. This is defined by the vector equations:

$$M = \int dm = \int \rho dV \qquad M\mathbf{r}_G = \int \mathbf{r} dm = \int \mathbf{r} \rho dV$$

where the integrals are taken over the whole of the body. M is the total mass of the body, $\mathbf{r}_G$ is the position vector of the centre of mass G, relative to some arbitrary origin, $\mathbf{r}$ is the position vector of an element of mass dm, relative to the same origin, ρ is the local density of the body and dV is an element of volume. The position of the centre of mass is a function only of the mass distribution (or the shape and density distribution) of the body.

For the (special, but common) case of a body of uniform density, the centre of mass coincides with the *Centre of Volume*, or *Centroid*, whose position is calculated using the above equations with volume in place of mass. This may be assumed to be the case, unless stated otherwise, in the rest of this book. The position of the centroid is a purely geometrical property of the shape of the body. For many shapes, it can readily be found by arguments of symmetry. For example, it lies at the centre of a sphere and at the crossing point of the body diagonals for a cuboid. For a cylinder, it is on the axis, at the mid-point of the length. Examples of methods of calculating the positions of centroids are given in Appendix II.

3.2 EQUILIBRIUM UNDER GRAVITY

The weight of a body can be considered as a single force acting downwards through the centre of gravity. (This is, in fact, the definition of the direction 'downwards'.) In principle, to satisfy equilibrium, we only need a single, co-linear, equal force in the opposite direction. But such a situation is rarely met, since it tends to be unstable. Any small horizontal movement of the body will usually lead to the forces ceasing to be co-linear, and a moment is produced which leads to the body rotating (i.e. it falls over). There are exceptions to this, for example a perfect sphere on a horizontal surface, but usually the support force must be either distributed over an area or split between at least two points, in a two dimensional situation, or at least three in three dimensions.

A body is said to be *simply supported* if it is supported by forces providing only one constraint at the minimum number of points required for equilibrium.

Since this number is the same as the number of equilibrium equations, the
support forces can be calculated uniquely. For example, the support forces for
the three-legged stool whose free body diagram is shown in Figure 3.1 can be
calculated.

The sum of the three
support forces must equal
the total weight:

$$S_1 + S_2 + S_3 = W$$

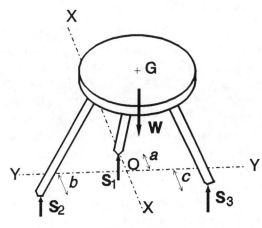

We define axes XOX and
YOY in the plane of the
floor, intersecting at a
point O, which is directly
below the centre of gravity
G, as shown. The weight
thus produces no moment
about either XOX or
YOY. The directions of
the axes are arbitrary, so

Figure 3.1

long as they do not coincide. For simplicity, we will take XOX such that it
passes through the base of leg 1 and is equidistant between legs 2 and 3, and
YOY perpendicular to it. Considering moments about the axis XOX, we obtain:

$$S_2 = S_3$$

Similarly, taking moments about the axis YOY:

$$S_1 a = S_2 b + S_3 c$$

These three equations in the three unknown forces S_1, S_2 and S_3 can be solved
provided the total weight **W** and the three dimensions a, b and c are known.

We can only solve problems of this kind for simply supported objects. If the
stool had less than three legs, it would be possible to find equilibrium
configurations, but these would be unstable. For most positions of the centre of
gravity and legs, equilibrium would be impossible.

Conversely, a four (or more) legged stool will probably be stable, but it is
not simply supported. In the calculation of the forces, we would have an extra
unknown, but no extra equations. Similarly, if the three legs lay in the same
straight line, we could find an unstable equilibrium position, as for the case of
two legs, but we would not be able to calculate the three support forces from the

two equations available. To find the support forces in such cases, we need at least one extra equation relating to the deflection of the stool and its supports when under load. We will consider this sort of situation in Part 2.

3.3 STRUCTURES

Frequently, a body is made up of several parts, joined together in some way. This is known as a *structure*. We may need to know the forces acting within and between the various parts. The parts are called *members*, and are connected together at *joints*. External *loads* (which include the weight of the members and support forces) may be applied either to the members themselves or through the joints.

In real structures, the members, joints and supports may be complex in shape and in the way they are fixed together. For example, joints may range from smoothly hinged connections through various semi-rigid bolted and riveted arrangements to essentially rigid welded or glued joints. Similarly, members may be straight uniform structural steel or wooden elements, or they may be complex metal, plastic or concrete castings or fabrications.

The detailed analysis of realistic structures can be extremely complex, but it is often possible to make some very sweeping simplifications which clarify how a particular structure works and how it may be designed to carry out a particular task. Such a simplified analysis can then, with appropriate theoretical or experimental *safety factors*, provide a useful engineering tool.

Here we will analyse some simple structures to find the loads carried by the various members. In Part 2 we will see how to calculate the deflections of the members under the loads and how to select dimensions and materials for those members so that they can carry the loads.

3.3.1 Idealized supports

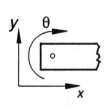

Figure 3.2

Any support system may provide up to 6 constraints: - it may prevent (or restrict) motion in any of the 3 co-ordinate directions, and it may prevent (or restrict) rotation about any of the 3 co-ordinate axes.

For simplicity, we will only consider 2 dimensional systems here. There are then 3 constraints: - motion in the x or y direction, and rotation about the z axis (see Figure 3.2, where the z direction is perpendicular to the xy plane shown). We will further assume that a constraint is either complete (no motion is possible) or absent (motion is unrestricted), and that a constraint works in both directions (a constraint for motion in the positive x direction also applies in the negative x direction, etc.).

Some idealized two-dimensional constraints are shown in Figure 3.3: (a) is a *built-in*, *fixed* or *encastré* support, and constrains all three motions; (b) is a *pin*, *knife edge* or *simple* support and constrains motion in the x and y directions; (c) is a *roller* support, and constrains motion in the y direction only, while (d) is a *slider* support, and constrains both motion in the y direction and rotation. Similarly, three-dimensional idealized constraints may be defined.

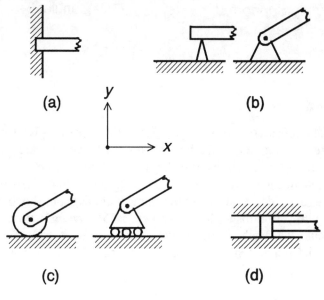

(a)

(b)

(c)

(d)

Figure 3.3

Note that these constraints are *kinematic* - they prevent motion. Whatever force (or moment) is necessary to do this is assumed to be available.

3.3.2 Idealized members

In two dimensions, quite useful results can be obtained by treating members as uniform beams (in three dimensions, plates are needed as well). Beams can be further sub-divided according to the way they carry loads - see Figure 3.4.

A *tie* is in tension, a *strut* is in compression, a *column* is a vertical strut, a *simply supported beam* and a *cantilever* carry transverse loads. Other combinations are also possible.

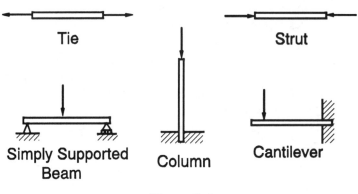

Figure 3.4

3.3.3 Idealized joints

Joints are often considered to be *pinned*, and allow free relative rotation. Since real joints are rarely pinned, but rather are bolted, welded, etc., this leads to significant errors in calculations near the joints. However, because such joining methods spread the load over a larger area than a pin, the errors are nearly always on the safe side. Away from the immediate neighbourhood of the joints, the errors quickly diminish (this is known as *St Venant's principle*, after a nineteenth century French engineer, who first pointed it out). The calculation assuming pinned joints, which is much more straightforward than alternatives, will show how the structure works, and generally lead to a conservative design.

3.3.4 Idealized loads

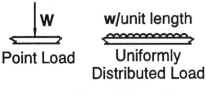

Figure 3.5

Similar arguments apply to loads as to both supports and joints. For simplicity, loads are usually considered to be either *point loads* or *uniformly distributed loads* (Figure 3.5).

3.4 STATIC DETERMINACY

In some structures, we can calculate all the forces in the members by considering the equilibrium of the members and of the pins in the joints. Consider, for example, the structure whose free body diagram is shown in Figure 3.6(a), in which the lines represent members and the circles perfect pin joints. External forces are applied at A and D. By equilibrium of the structure as a whole, F_1 must be equal to F_2. At each joint, we can draw the free body diagram for the pin. Figure 3.6(b) shows the diagram for joint A. Note the convention that tensions are positive. All bars are assumed to

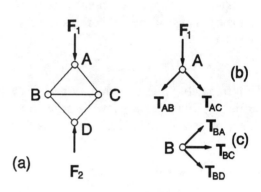

Figure 3.6

be in tension. If the result comes out negative, it must be in compression. Knowing F_1 and the angles, we can calculate T_{AB} and T_{AC}. We can then solve at B (Figure 3.6(c)) to get T_{BC} and T_{BD}, noting that $T_{AB} = T_{BA}$, by equilibrium of member AB. Similarly at C and D, thus finding all our bar forces. This structure is said to be *statically determinate* - all the forces can be calculated from equilibrium alone.

But compare this with the structure in Figure 3.7(a). There is no problem at A, but at B, we cannot get equilibrium. This is not a structure, it is a mechanism.

On the other hand, for Figure 3.7(b), we cannot even solve at A. (Note the convention that AD and BC cross without interfering with each other if no joint is drawn.) There are too many unknowns. This structure is *statically indeterminate*. The

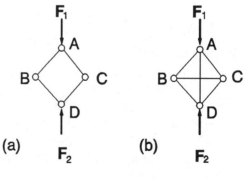

Figure 3.7

forces cannot be calculated from statics alone, but need consideration of deflections under loads (beyond our scope here). An alternative term for this is *redundant* - one or more members could be removed (any one member in this particular case) without it becoming a mechanism (it might or might not then be statically determinate).

In the general case, for a two dimensional structure with j joints and m members, we have $2j$ equations. As well as the m unknown bar forces, we have 3 unknown external reactions (one each in the x and y directions, and a moment). Thus, if the structure is to be statically determinate (or *just stiff*), we must have

$$m + 3 = 2j$$

Unfortunately, this criterion is necessary but not sufficient. Figure 3.8 shows a structure satisfying this, part of which is redundant and part of which is a mechanism.

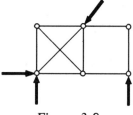

Figure 3.8

On the other hand, if

$$m + 3 < 2j$$

we have a mechanism (or *under stiff* structure), and if

$$m + 3 > 2j$$

we have a statically indeterminate, redundant or *over stiff* structure.

The equivalent relationships for a three-dimensional structure are

$$m + 6 = 3j,\quad \text{etc.}$$

3.5 FRAMEWORKS

A structure consisting of pin jointed members, with external loads and supports applied at the joints, is known as a *framework* or *truss*. If a framework is statically determinate, there are many straightforward methods of calculating the forces in the various members. Frequently, the design load will be much larger than the weights of the individual members, so these are ignored. Otherwise, they could either be included via the equilibrium equations of the members, or treated as additional external loads applied at the joints at each end of the member concerned.

Example

Consider the framework in Figure 3.9, which is a simplified two-dimensional model of one arm of an electricity transmission tower:

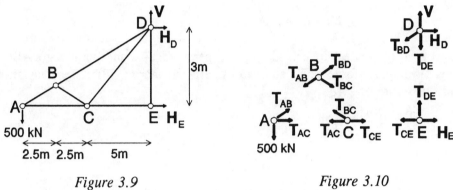

Figure 3.9   Figure 3.10

The load of 500 kN represents the weight of the conductors and insulators, the loads at the right hand side represent the support forces provided by the vertical part of the tower. For static determinacy, we must make some assumption about how the vertical component **V** of the support force is distributed between points D and E; we have arbitrarily taken it as all being applied at D.

The first stage in the solution of this (or any) framework problem is to find the support forces (reactions). Looking at vertical forces, it is clear that **V** = 500 kN, since there are no others. For horizontal forces, similarly, $\mathbf{H_D} = -\mathbf{H_E}$. Taking moments about E gives:

$$3\mathbf{H_D} = 10 \times 500 \text{ kN m, or } \mathbf{H_D} = 1667 \text{ kN, and } \mathbf{H_E} = -1667 \text{ kN}$$

We could have equally well taken moments about D, or indeed any other point. The equations would have been different, but their solutions the same.

We find the forces in the members by drawing free body diagrams for the pins, as in Figure 3.10. Remember the convention that tensile forces are positive. We do not need to distinguish between $\mathbf{T_{AB}}$ and $\mathbf{T_{BA}}$, etc, since we are neglecting the weight of the members. We can look at the vertical and horizontal equilibrium of various pins:

At joint E:

↑ $\mathbf{T_{DE}} = 0$ (no load)

→ $\mathbf{T_{CE}} = \mathbf{H_E}$
$= -1667$ kN (compression).

At A:

    ↑ $T_{AB} \sin\theta = 500$ kN (where θ is the angle DAE), so that
        $T_{AB} = 1740$ kN (tension)

    → $T_{AB} \cos\theta + T_{AC} = 0$, whence
        $T_{AC} = -1667$ kN (compression).

At B it is convenient to consider forces perpendicular and parallel to ABD. There is only one force with a component perpendicular to ABD: T_{BC}. The latter must therefore be zero.

    ⌐ $T_{BC} = 0$, so that
    ‖ $T_{BD} = T_{AB} = 1740$ kN

At C:

    Since $T_{AC} = T_{CE}$ (already found), and $T_{BC} = 0$, $T_{CD} = 0$.

We have thus found all the forces in the members. While in this particular case, three of them have turned out to carry no load, this does not necessarily mean that this framework is unrealistic. Remember that we have ignored the weights of the members, assumed that all the vertical load is taken at D, and only considered a vertical load at A. Other loading patterns will arise in practise, for example due to wind loading or at corners in the transmission line. The 'extra' members may then take load.

This framework was solved by and large by inspection, and this is usually quite satisfactory for small, simple, two dimensional frameworks. Often, many alternative sequences are possible. However for larger, more complex, three dimensional frameworks, more systematic methods are needed. Many have been developed, some graphical and some algebraic. However, all framework problems can be reduced to the solution of $3j$ simultaneous equations of equilibrium in $m + 6$ unknowns. Such problems are well suited to computers and matrix methods, and general computer programs which can solve arbitrary statically determinate frameworks are widely available.

EXAMPLES

It is suggested that the first part of Appendix II is studied before these problems are attempted.

3.1 By direct integration, find the positions of the centroids of (a) a semi-circle of radius R, (b) a circular segment of radius R, subtending an angle 2θ, (c) a semi-circular arc of inside radius r_1 and outside radius r_2. (Ans: (a) $4R/3\pi$ from diameter, (b) $2R\sin^3\theta/3(\theta - \sin\theta\cos\theta)$ from centre, (c) $4(r_2^3 - r_1^3)/3\pi(r_2^2 - r_1^2)$ from diameter.)

3.2 By combination of shapes, find the positions of the centroids of the shapes shown in Figure 3.11.

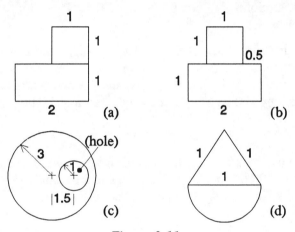

Figure 3.11

(Ans: (a) 5/6 from bottom and right edges, (b) 5/6 from bottom edge, on axis of symmetry, (c) 3/16 to left of centre of large circle, on line joining centres, (d) 0.05 above diameter, on axis of symmetry)

3.3 What is the maximum overhang possible when four bricks are stacked on top of each other? Is there any limit to the overhang possible with a very large number of bricks?
(Ans: 11/12 times the length of a brick. No.)

3.4 A door is 2 m high and 0.9 m wide, and has a mass of 15 kg. It is supported on two hinges 15 cm from the top and the bottom respectively. Assuming that the top hinge takes no weight, calculate the support forces provided by the hinges. Assume that the weight of the door acts at its centre.

(Ans: Top hinge 39.0 N inwards (towards doorpost), bottom hinge 147 N upwards and 39.0 N outwards.)

3.5   A vertical aerial mast 20 m high is subjected to a horizontal load of 1000 N due West from the aerial wire at the top. It is pin jointed at its base, and supported by two cables from the top to anchor points on the ground 5 m from the base, in North-Easterly and South-Easterly directions. Calculate the forces in the mast and stay cables, and the reaction force supplied by the base support.

(Ans: 5656 N, compression; 2915 N tension; 5656 N vertically upwards.)

3.6   Four lamps, each of mass 2 kg, are supported above a street by a light cord between two posts 20 m apart. The lamps are equally spaced horizontally between the posts, and the two centre lamps are 4 m below the tops of the posts. Calculate the tensions in the various sections of the cable.

(Ans: 70.7 N, 62.0 N, 58.9 N, 62.0 N, 70.7 N)

3.7   A power station chimney is 150 m high and 10 m diameter, and of total mass 20 000 tonnes. Wind forces exert a uniformly distributed load of 3.8 kN m^{-1} along its length. What reaction forces must its foundations provide?

(Ans: A vertically upward force of 196 MN, a horizontal upwind force of 570 kN, a moment of 42.8 MN m tending to rotate the top upwind.)

3.8   Calculate the external reactions and all the member forces for the framework shown in Figure 3.12. All the diagonal members are at 45°.

(Ans: 10 kN downwards at A, 20 kN upwards at B, no horizontal reaction. $T_{AB}=0$, $T_{EB}=-20$ kN, $T_{AE}=0$, $T_{AC}=10$ kN, $T_{DF}=10\sqrt{2}$ kN, $T_{EF}=-10$ kN, $T_{CD}=10\sqrt{2}$ kN. $T_{CE}=-10$ kN, $T_{DE}=-20$ kN)

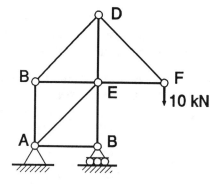

Figure 3.12

3.9 A square pin-jointed framework is braced by two diagonals. One of them contains a tensioner which is adjusted to a tension T. What are the forces in the other members?
(Ans: Sides $-T/\sqrt{2}$, other diagonal T)

3.10 By inspection, find all the forces in the members of the pin-jointed framework shown in Figure 3.13.

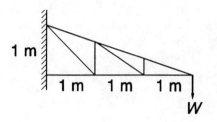

Figure 3.13

BIBLIOGRAPHY

Meriam JL, *Statics*. Wiley, 1980 (Chapters 3-5)
Benham PP and Crawford RJ, *Mechanics of Engineering Materials*. Longman, 1987 (Chapter 1)

4

Kinematics

Kinematics is the study of motion by itself. If any massive bodies undergo accelerations, forces must exist, but this is not the realm of kinematics. It is solely concerned with the relationships between accelerations, velocities and positions. Any forces required are assumed to be available.

4.1 CONSTANT ACCELERATION

Constant acceleration occurs when a constant force acts on a body of constant mass. The most common situations where this happens are motion under gravity, neglecting air resistance and other secondary effects, and approximately, motion under dry sliding friction (see Chapter 6). If either the force is not constant or the mass varies, the acceleration will not be constant. Varying forces are considered below. Varying mass (e.g. in vehicles where fuel is consumed or cases where liquid evaporation or ice deposition occurs) is not considered in this book.

The equation of motion for constant acceleration may be written

$$\ddot{x} = \frac{\mathbf{F}}{M} = const$$

Leaving this in terms of the acceleration, rather than the force and mass, makes it a kinematic equation, rather than a dynamic one.

Integrating this with respect to time, we obtain the velocity:

$$\dot{x} = \dot{x}_0 + \ddot{x}t$$

where $\dot{x}_0$ is the velocity at time $t = 0$.

Alternatively, we can integrate with respect to position (making use of the identity $\ddot{x} = \dot{x}\dfrac{d\dot{x}}{dx}$), and obtain:

$$\dot{x}^2 = \dot{x}_0^2 + 2\ddot{x}(x - x_0)$$

where x_0 is the position at time $t = 0$. The same result can be obtained by multiplying through by an integrating factor $2\dot{x}$, and integrating with respect to time.

Other useful forms may be obtained by integrating again, and substituting various equations into each other. Examples are:

$$x = x_0 + \dot{x}_0 t + \frac{1}{2}\ddot{x}t^2$$

$$x = x_0 + \frac{\dot{x} + \dot{x}_0}{2}t$$

It must be remembered that these equations are only valid if the acceleration is constant.

Example

A lift of mass 1000 kg is counter-balanced by an equal mass, and carries a load of 200 kg. The lift is released from rest. Neglecting air resistance and friction and inertia effects in the pulley, how fast is it moving after it has fallen 10 m?

Figure 4.1(a) shows the system diagram. Figures 4.1(b) and (c) show the free-body diagrams for the lift and the balance weight, respectively. **T** is the tension in the lift cable (which is assumed to be the same on both sides of the pulley). Note the two different coordinates, x_1 and x_2, which specify the positions of the lift and balance weight, respectively.

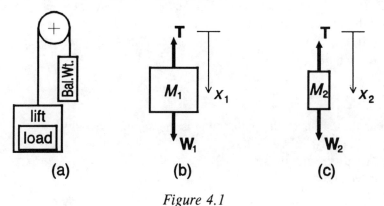

Figure 4.1

The equations of motion of the lift and the balance weight are:

$$M_1\ddot{x}_1 = W_1 - T \qquad\qquad M_2\ddot{x}_2 = W_2 - T$$

We can eliminate the cable tension **T** between these equations. Also, we know that $x_1 + x_2$ must be constant (if one goes up, the other goes down the same distance), so that $\ddot{x}_1 = -\ddot{x}_2$. The weights are given by $\mathbf{W}_1 = M_1 g$ and $\mathbf{W}_2 = M_2 g$, so that the final overall equation of motion is

$$\ddot{x}_1 = \frac{M_1 - M_2}{M_1 + M_2} g$$

The acceleration is thus constant, so the equations above may be used. Putting in the numerical values given at the start gives the required velocity, 4.22 m s^{-1}.

4.2 MOTION IN A CIRCLE

A body travelling round a circular path is subject to an acceleration (and thus forces must act on it). A body on the surface of the earth is moving in a circular path - gravity keeps it on the surface. If there was no gravitational force, the body would move in a straight line - a tangent to the surface.

   The acceleration of the body is a purely kinematic requirement. For simplicity, we will only consider uniform motion about a circular path. Including tangential accelerations and radial velocities and accelerations is not difficult, but complicates the issue without introducing any really new principles.

Consider the body in Figure 4.2(a). At a particular instant t it is at position B_1 (given by an angular coordinate θ), and has velocity $\mathbf{v}_1$. A short time dt later, it is at B_2 ($\theta + d\theta$) with velocity $\mathbf{v}_2$. The velocity magnitudes v_1 and v_2 are equal; it is only the direction of motion which has changed. The velocity magnitudes are given by:

$$v_1 = v_2 = v = r\frac{d\theta}{dt} = r\omega$$

where r is the radius of the path and ω is the angular velocity.

Figure 4.2(b) shows the velocity vectors, and illustrates the vector equation

$$\mathbf{v}_2 = \mathbf{v}_1 + d\mathbf{v}$$

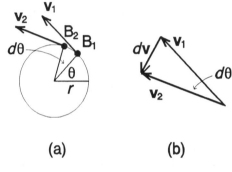

The vector $d\mathbf{v}$ is the change in velocity which has occurred in time dt. In terms of magnitudes,

$$dv = vd\theta$$

$$\frac{dv}{dt} = v\frac{d\theta}{dt} = v\omega = \frac{v^2}{r} = \omega^2 r$$

(a)   **(b)**

Figure 4.2

The acceleration given by this last equation is, from Figure 4.2(b), directed towards the centre of the circle. For motion in a circle to exist, a force (the *centripetal* force) must be provided.

Example

What acceleration is experienced by an armature conductor of small diameter at a radius of 50 cm in an alternator rotating at 1500 rev min^{-1} ?

Using the notation above,

$$\omega = \frac{1500}{60} \times 2\pi = 157.1 \text{ s}^{-1}$$

$$\text{acceleration} = \omega^2 r = 12\ 337 \text{ m s}^{-2}$$
(or about 1258 times the acceleration due to gravity)

4.3 VARIABLE ACCELERATION

Variable acceleration problems are by far the most common in real life. Unfortunately, they are also often the most complex to solve. Frequently, instead of a simple integration to find the velocity or position, it will be necessary to solve a differential equation, or simultaneous differential equations. In some simple one and two dimensional situations, there may be analytical solutions to particular problems, but frequently this is not the case and numerical or graphical solutions must be sought.

It must, of course, be known how and with what variables the acceleration varies. For example, it may vary as a function of position, time, or some other quantity. The variation may be linear, or have many other characteristics. As an example, we will consider here a simple case where the acceleration varies linearly with position.

Let us consider a mass on the end of a spring, whose other end is fixed (and ignore any other forces which might be acting on the mass). Applications are many, but we may mention computer keys, door latches, vehicle suspensions.

Assume that the spring is *linear*, that is, it exerts a force which is directly proportional to distance from some origin*. Further, it is in the nature of springs that the force is directed towards that origin. A compression spring tends to push things away, while a tension spring draws them in.

The situation is thus as in Figure 4.3: the spring force **F** is given by

$$\mathbf{F} = -kx$$

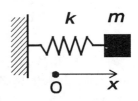

where k is called the *spring stiffness*, and is, for a linear spring, a constant over some range of position x, measured from an origin O at the unstretched position of the end of the spring. **F** is directed in the negative x direction. The equation of motion of the mass m is

Figure 4.3

$$m\ddot{x} = -kx, \text{ or } \ddot{x} = -\frac{k}{m}x$$

Since m and k are constants, this is a kinematic equation, and the acceleration varies proportionally to x. Assuming that the mass starts from rest at time $t = 0$, the solution to this equation is

$$x = x_0 \cos \left[\left[\frac{k}{m} \right]^{0.5} t \right]$$

where x_0 is the position at time $t = 0$.

An equation of this form implies an oscillatory motion - we shall see a good deal more of it and discuss its various forms of solution in Chapter 5. Not all the applications mentioned above are oscillatory; this is because we ignored other forces which will always be present; our model is incomplete. For example, the bolt of the door latch will initially accelerate out under the action of its compressed spring (ignoring friction effects). However, when the spring reaches approximately zero compression and is about to go into tension, the bolt (which is by then travelling at its maximum velocity) will hit its end stop, and be brought to rest.

EXAMPLES

4.1   A balloon of mass M descends with downward acceleration f_1. Neglecting air resistance, what mass of ballast should be thrown out in order that it should rise with upward acceleration f_2? (Assume the buoyancy force is constant.)
        (Ans: $M(f_1 + f_2)/(g + f_2)$)

4.2   The balloon in question 4.1 is descending at 3 m s^{-1}. The ballast takes 5 s to fall to the ground. What is the height of the balloon? (Ignore air resistance).
        (Ans: 138 m)

4.3   A proton of mass 1.66×10^{-27} kg travelling horizontally a 3×10^6 m s^{-1} enters a uniform electric field which exerts a side force on it of 6×10^{-15} N, and extends over a distance of 0.5 m. Through what angle is the proton deflected?
        (Ans: $11° \, 21'$)

4.4   Two solid steel balls 1 m diameter are freely suspended with a gap of 1 mm between them. Estimate how long they will take to come together under their mutual gravitational attraction. How will this time depend on the diameter of the balls, assuming the initial spacing remains at 1 mm? (Use the form of the law of gravitation given in Chapter 2.) (Ans: 1 minute approx)

4.5 A racing car travels round a bend of radius 500 m. Its tyres can produce a sideways force of at most 80% of the weight of the car. What is the maximum speed it can drive without skidding? (62.6 m s^{-1})

4.6 An electric charge q moving at velocity v through a magnetic field of strength H experiences a force $F = \mu_0 Hqv$ at right angles to the direction of motion. μ_0 is a constant. Calculate the radius of the path of an electron travelling at 2×10^7 m s^{-1} through the earth's magnetic field, which is of strength 4.8×10^{-7} SI units. The charge on an electron is 1.6×10^{-19} SI units and its mass is 9.1×10^{-31} kg. $\mu_0 = 4\pi \times 10^{-7}$ SI units. Ignore relativistic effects. (Ans: 1886 km)

4.7 An aircraft flies along a curved trajectory to simulate weightlessness in the cabin. At the top of the trajectory, the radius of curvature of the path is 7500 m. What speed should the aircraft fly at? (Ans: 271 m s^{-1} = 976 km h^{-1})

4.8 A car's gears are usable in the following speed ranges, and can produce the accelerations shown:

First:	0 - 45 km h^{-1}	3.5 m s^{-2}
Second:	35 - 90 km h^{-1}	4.5 m s^{-2}
Third:	65 - 130 km h^{-1}	3 m s^{-2}

What is the minimum time required to accelerate from rest to 130 km h^{-1}, and at what speeds should the driver change gear to achieve this? (Ans: 9.88 s, 35 and 90 km h^{-1})

4.9 The air drag on a parachute is given by $D = 56v^2$, where D is the drag in newtons and v is the speed in metres per second. What is the maximum speed with which a parachutist of all-up mass 100 kg can hit the ground? (Ans: 4.2 m s^{-1})

4.10 A vehicle of mass 1 tonne experiences drag forces of $12v$ due to internal friction and $0.5v^2$ due to aerodynamic drag (both in SI units). It starts from rest and runs freely down a hill of slope 1:10. Calculate how far it travels before aerodynamic drag becomes the larger force, and how long this takes. (Ans: 280 m, 23.3 s)

BIBLIOGRAPHY

Collinson CD, *Introductory Mechanics*. Edward Arnold, 1980 (Chapter 3)
Smith RC and Smith P, *Mechanics*. Wiley, 1971 (Chapter 2)

5

Simple Harmonic Motion

At the end of Chapter 4, we briefly considered the motion of a mass attached to a spring, and saw that, on very simple assumptions, the motion was periodic. In fact, any system with both mass and stiffness is likely to move in a periodic manner. Such a system is a *vibrator* or *oscillator*. In some situations, the periodic motion is deliberately induced, while in others it is definitely detrimental to the primary function of the system. Vibrating systems arise in all fields of engineering and physics, ranging from electromagnetic wave propagation through acoustics and electronics to machine tools and clocks. There is frequently a close enough analogy for one of these systems to be used as a model for another.

As we will see below, a vibrating system has a characteristic frequency of oscillation, know as the *natural frequency*. If the system is disturbed, and then allowed to move at its natural frequency, the motion is called *free vibration*. If, alternatively, the disturbance is maintained, and is itself periodic, the system will move in a combination of its own natural motion and that imposed by the disturbance. This is called *forced vibration*.

5.1 FREE VIBRATION

5.1.1 Linear and non-linear oscillators

In the example of Chapter 4, the spring was taken as linear. This is not necessary for oscillation to occur, but the mathematics of non-linear oscillators is complex, and we will confine ourselves to linear systems. It is often possible for a system which is strictly non-linear to be approximated as linear under certain restricted conditions. For example, Figure 5.1 shows a simple pendulum, and the free body diagram of its bob. The acceleration of the bob is $L\ddot{\theta}$, while the component of the weight in the tangential direction is $mg\sin\theta$. The equation of motion in the tangential direction (the only direction in which we need to consider the motion) is thus

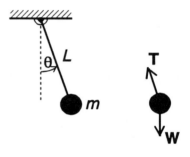

$$\ddot{\theta} + \frac{g}{L}\sin\theta = 0$$

Figure 5.1

This equation is non-linear. The acceleration does not vary linearly with the displacement. However, for small angles, it is common to assume that $\sin\theta = \theta$ (this is accurate to 1% up to about 17°, and to 0.5% up to about 10°). With this substitution, the equation of motion becomes

$$\ddot{\theta} + \frac{g}{L}\theta = 0$$

which is linear, and in fact structurally identical to the equation for a spring-mass system.

5.1.2 Degrees of Freedom

The spring-mass system and the pendulum are single degree of freedom systems. Their configuration can be defined in terms of a single coordinate. But consider the systems in Figure 5.2: both these have two degrees of freedom. Whereas our one degree of freedom oscillator will vibrate at one natural frequency (as we will see below), the two degree of freedom one will have two natural frequencies. If we draw free-body diagrams for the two masses, and write down the equations of motion, we will obtain a pair of simultaneous differential equations in the two coordinate variables. Their solution presents no real difficulty in this particular case (or in similar cases with more than two degrees of freedom), however, we will confine our attention to single degree of freedom systems.

5.1.3 Lumped parameters

In the above pendulum example, and in the spring example in Chapter 4, we tacitly assumed that all the mass was in the pendulum bob or weight, and that the pendulum rod and spring

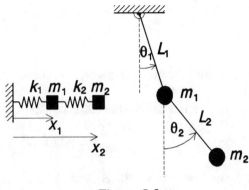

Figure 5.2

were massless. Such an assumption is called a *lumped parameter model*. It can never be completely correct, but is often a good approximation; it greatly simplifies the analysis. As we saw above, if we divide the mass and flexibility of the system into two parts, we get two degrees of freedom and two natural frequencies. Similarly, if the mass and stiffness are both distributed throughout our system, we will get an infinite number of degrees of freedom and natural frequencies. There are many cases where this has to be done, for example cantilever structures and many types of musical instrument. But to understand the basics of vibrating systems, it is perfectly adequate to confine ourselves to lumped parameter models with a finite number of degrees of freedom.

5.1.4 The equation of motion

The equation of free motion for an undamped single degree of freedom system can be written:

$$\ddot{x} + \omega_n^2 x = 0$$

where ω_n is a characteristic constant which depends on the physical parameters of the system. For the spring-mass system of Chapter 4, it is given by:

$$\omega_n^2 = \frac{k}{m}$$

while for the (linearized) pendulum of Figure 5.1, it is:

$$\omega_n^2 = \frac{g}{L}$$

ω_n is called the circular natural frequency or *radiancy*; its units are radians per second (rad s^{-1}).

The general solution of this equation is:

$$x = A\sin\omega_n t + B\cos\omega_n t$$

The two constants A and B are mathematically arbitrary: any values whatsoever will satisfy the equation of motion. Physically, however, they are very far from arbitrary. It is their values which make one vibrating system different from another. They can be found by knowledge of two pieces of information about the motion, often the initial conditions. For example, if the displacement x is zero at time $t = 0$, then B must be zero. If, further, the maximum displacement reached during the motion is X_0, then $A = X_0$. Any two independent pieces of information about position, velocity or acceleration at particular times could be used in a similar fashion.

There are several alternative ways of writing this solution. One which makes the behaviour more obvious is to write:

$$A = X_0\cos\phi \qquad \text{and} \qquad B = X_0\sin\phi$$

so that the above becomes:

$$x = X_0(\cos\phi \sin\omega_n t + \sin\phi \cos\omega_n t)$$

$$\text{or} \qquad x = X_0\sin(\omega_n t + \phi)$$

This still has two "arbitrary" constants, X_0 and ϕ, which are found in a similar manner to A and B. X_0 is called the *amplitude* of vibration, and ϕ is called the *phase angle, lead, lag* or *epoch*. Note, however, that various authors will use two or more of these terms simultaneously with minor differences in meaning. For example, *lag* may be treated as a negative *lead*. The exact definitions of the terms should always be sought in the same text as their use - there is no agreed standard.

The motion described by this equation is harmonic with period $T = 2\pi/\omega_n$ (units: seconds), and natural frequency $f_n = \omega_n/2\pi = 1/T$ (units: Hz). Because the variation of position with time is sinusoidal (see Figure 5.3), it is described as *simple harmonic*.

Example

A spring balance has a 5 cm long linear scale from 0 to 10 kg. What will be its natural frequency of vibration when a weight of mass 5 kg is placed on it?

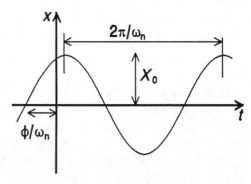

Figure 5.3

When fully extended, the load on the balance would be $10g$ N. The spring stiffness k is therefore $10g/0.05$ N m^{-1} = 1962 N m^{-1}. With the 5 kg mass ($5g$ N weight), ω_n is therefore given by $\omega_n = \sqrt{(k/m)} = 19.81$ rad s^{-1}. $f_n = \omega_n/2\pi = 3.15$ Hz. The period is $1/f_n = 0.32$ s.

All simple harmonic single degree of freedom systems have a very similar behaviour, and their characteristics can often be used to estimate, at least qualitatively, the behaviour of more complex systems. In particular, they all have a natural frequency which is independent of amplitude*, and which increases directly as the square root of the stiffness, and inversely as the square root of mass or inertia.

There are thus two ways of modifying the natural frequency of a system: change the stiffness, or change the inertia. For example, the spring balance in the example above will have a natural frequency of 2.23 Hz ($3.15/\sqrt{2}$ Hz) when carrying its full load of $10g$ N, while another balance covering the same range with half the scale length would have a natural frequency of 4.45 Hz ($3.15\sqrt{2}$ Hz) under the load of $5g$ N.

Both these methods can be seen in the tuning of musical instruments, such as violins or pianos. The strings which are required to produce lower notes are made of thicker or denser material (increasing the mass), and may be longer (reducing the stiffness) than those for higher notes. Fine tuning is carried out by adjusting the tension, which changes the stiffness. The vibration of such strings is not usually simple harmonic, single degree of freedom, but the same principles apply.

---

* In reality, there must always be some amplitude where the spring, or equivalent, becomes non-linear. For example, it may deform permanently or break, or the mass may hit an end stop. The motion then ceases to be simple harmonic.

5.1.5 Effects of gravity

Up to now, we have tacitly assumed that gravity is not involved. However, for any vibration which has a component of movement in the vertical direction, gravity will add an extra force in the free body diagram, and so must be included.

Let us consider the vertical spring-mass system shown in Figure 5.4. Here, we have defined our x-coordinate to be positive downwards, and have its origin at the height of the suspension point of the spring. We have also defined two additional points: x_0, which is the position of the end of the spring when unloaded (i.e. no compression or tension); and x_1, which is the position of the mass in equilibrium (i.e. no velocity or acceleration).

The spring force T is given by:

$$T = k(x - x_0)$$

and, from the free body diagram in Figure 5.4, the equation of motion is:

$$m\ddot{x} = mg - k(x - x_0)$$

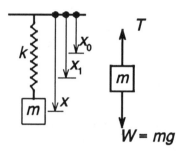

Figure 5.4

When the whole system is stationary, $\ddot{x} = 0$ and $x = x_1$, so that:

$$mg = k(x_1 - x_0)$$

combining the two above equations:

$$m\ddot{x} = k(x_1 - x_0) - k(x - x_0)$$

$$= k(x_1 - x)$$

Introducing a new coordinate $y = x - x_1$ = distance from the equilibrium position, and rearranging, we obtain:

$$m\ddot{y} + ky = 0 \qquad \omega_n^2 = \frac{k}{m} \qquad \text{as before.}$$

We see, then, that the only effect of gravity is to move the position of the mid-point of the motion: it now takes place about the equilibrium position, rather than the unstretched position. It has no effect on the frequency. If we always measure our displacement from the equilibrium position, we do not need to bring gravity into the equations explicitly.

We can also use the equilibrium equation to calculate the natural frequency without needing to calculate the spring stiffness explicitly:

$$\omega_n^2 = \frac{k}{m} = \frac{mg}{x_1 - x_0} \times \frac{1}{m} = \frac{g}{\text{static deflection}}$$

Example

A crane lifts a load, and its cable stretches 0.1 m. Calculate the natural frequency of vertical oscillations of the load on the cable.

$$\omega_n^2 = \frac{g}{\text{static deflection}} = \frac{9.81}{0.1} \text{ rad}^2 \text{ s}^{-2}$$

$$\therefore \omega_n = 9.9 \text{ rad/s} \qquad f_n = 1.58 \text{ Hz}$$

5.2 FORCED VIBRATION

In many, probably most, real vibration situations, the oscillator is subject to a disturbance which may itself be a function of time, and is often approximately periodic. For example, the drum of a washing machine is often spring mounted, and its natural frequency depends on the spring stiffness and the mass of the drum and its contents. Since it will never be completely symmetrically loaded, it is subject to disturbing forces at its rotational speed, and probably also at the rotational speeds of other components of the machine.

We will consider three types of disturbance (or *excitation*): firstly, where a sinusoidally varying force of constant amplitude is applied to the mass. This could arise, for example, if the mass was a magnetic material in the field of a solenoid excited by alternating current. This is known as *constant excitation*. Secondly, the above situation where the disturbance arises from an out of balance mass, known as *inertial excitation*, and thirdly where it arises from a movement of the spring support point or ground, *seismic excitation*.

5.2.1 Constant excitation

The free body diagram in this case is shown in Figure 5.5, where F_0 is the amplitude of the disturbing force, and ω its circular frequency (the frequency f is given by $\omega/2\pi$).

The equation of motion is therefore:

$$m\ddot{x} = F_0\cos\omega t - kx$$

or $m\ddot{x} + kx = F_0\cos\omega t$

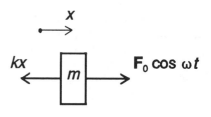

Figure 5.5

The solution to this equation consists of the sum of two terms: the *complementary function*, which is the solution when $F_0 = 0$ (i.e. the same as the free vibration solution), and the *particular integral*, which is any function which satisfies the whole equation.

To find the particular integral, we assume that the response will be at the same frequency as the forcing function. We look for a solution of the form:

$$x = X\cos\omega t$$

Substituting this into the equation of motion, we obtain:

$$-m\omega^2 X + kX = F_0$$

(where we have divided through by the $\cos\omega t$ term). From this, we obtain an expression for X:

$$X = \frac{F_0}{k - m\omega^2} = \frac{X_0}{1 - (\frac{\omega}{\omega_n})^2}$$

where $X_0 = F_0/k$ and we have substituted $\omega_n^2 = k/m$ as before. The complete solution of the equation of motion is therefore:

$$x = A\sin\omega_n t + B\cos\omega_n t + \frac{X_0\cos\omega t}{1 - (\frac{\omega}{\omega_n})^2}$$

The constants A and B are found from initial or other conditions in the same way as for free vibrations.

This motion can be shown, by straightforward trigonometrical methods, to be a sinusoidal oscillation at the average of the natural and forcing frequencies, which is modulated in amplitude at the difference between the two frequencies (Figure 5.6)

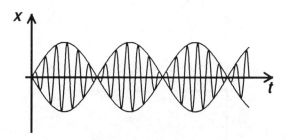

Figure 5.6

This amplitude variation at the difference frequency is known as *beating*.

Although beating as described above does exist and can be demonstrated, it is often not particularly important in practise. This is because the part of the motion represented by the complementary function (the free vibration element) tends to decrease in amplitude with time, due to energy loss through friction, air resistance, etc. (this will be fully discussed in Chapter 6). The part represented by the particular integral, however, has energy fed into it from whatever is causing the excitation, so that it does not die away. So after a period of time, only the latter motion remains (the values of A and B have both become zero), and the motion is at the forcing frequency only. Because of this behaviour, the free vibration component is often called the *transient* component, and the forced one the *steady state*.

When the transient has died away, we obtain the steady state solution:

$$x = \frac{X_0}{1 - (\frac{\omega}{\omega_n})^2} \cos\omega t = X\cos\omega t$$

We can plot the amplitude ratio X/X_0 against the frequency ratio ω/ω_n to obtain the *frequency response* (Figure 5.7):

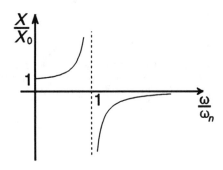

Figure 5.7

When the exciting frequency is much less than the natural frequency, the steady state oscillation is in phase with the exciting force, and of amplitude $X_0 = F_0/k$. Conversely, when the exciting frequency is much greater than the natural frequency, the steady state response is small, but out of phase with the excitation. In between, the amplitude can become very large. This is called *resonance*. We will consider resonance in more detail below, after looking at the other two forms of excitation.

5.2.2 Inertial excitation

A rotating mass has an acceleration towards the centre of rotation which depends on the square of angular velocity (Section 4.2). It thus imposes a force on the axis of rotation which is also proportional to the square of angular velocity, and which rotates with the mass. In a single degree of freedom system, we assume that the "lateral" component of this force is absorbed in some way, and we are left with the "longitudinal" component, which will vary sinusoidally at the rotation frequency.

The equation of motion is:

$$m\ddot{x} = C\omega^2\cos\omega t - kx$$

$$\text{or} \quad m\ddot{x} + kx = C\omega^2\cos\omega t$$

where C is a constant related to the amount of the out of balance mass and its location. Since ω is constant, the amplitude ratio of the steady state solution is:

$$\frac{X}{X_0} = \frac{(\frac{\omega}{\omega_n})^2}{1 - (\frac{\omega}{\omega_n})^2}$$

where $X_0 = C/m$.

The frequency response curve for this case is shown in Figure 5.8; in general character, it is similar to that for constant excitation, and again shows resonance when the forcing frequency is equal to the natural frequency. At low forcing frequencies, however, the response is small, while at very high frequencies it tends to a constant amplitude.

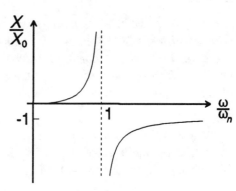

Figure 5.8

Example

A machine is supported on flexible mountings which deflect by 1 mm under the static weight of the machine. At what rotational speed should the machine not run?

From Section 5.1.5, the natural circular frequency is $\sqrt{(g/\text{static deflection})}$ = $\sqrt{(9.81/0.001)}$ = 99.05 rad s⁻¹. This will also be the resonant frequency, and is equivalent to $99.05/2\pi$ = 15.8 rev s⁻¹ or 946 rev min⁻¹.

5.2.3 Seismic Excitation

In many situations, the effective anchor point of the spring may move. An example is a vehicle suspension: the mass of the vehicle is supported on springs, the other ends of which are effectively supported by the road. If the vehicle travels over a bumpy road, the spring support points move. The system then appears as in Figure 5.9 (where gravity has been ignored, but could be included just as in Section 5.1.5, above).

The equation of motion is:

$$m\ddot{x} = -k(x - x_0)$$

and if $x_0 = X_0\cos\omega t$,

$$m\ddot{x} + kx = kX_0\cos\omega t$$

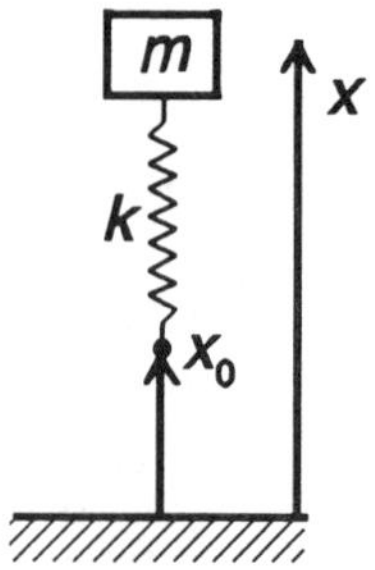

This is identical to the equation for constant
excitation, Section 5.2.1 above, and so the solution
is also the same and the response is as on Figure
5.7.

Example

A car of mass 1000 kg *is mounted on four springs*
each of stiffness 3×10^4 N m^{-1}. *Its shock absorbers*
are defective, and do not apply any force. Calculate its natural frequency of
vertical vibrations and the amplitude of vibrations when it drives at 30 km h^{-1}
along an undulating road with a wavelength of 3 m *and a peak to trough height*
of 10 cm.

Figure 5.9

We assume that one quarter of the weight is supported on each of the
springs. The natural frequency is then $\omega_n = \sqrt{(k/m)} = \sqrt{(3 \times 10^4/250)} =$
10.95 rad s^{-1}, $f_n = \omega_n/2\pi = 1.74$ Hz.

The road applies a seismic excitation of amplitude $X_0 = 0.05$ m, at a
frequency f = speed/wavelength = $(30 \times 10^3/3600)/3 = 2.78$ Hz. $\omega = 2.78 \times 2\pi$
= 17.45 rad s^{-1}. $\omega/\omega_n = 1.59$. The amplitude ratio $X/X_0 = -1.65$, and the
amplitude will be 0.082 m (82 mm), out of phase with the road undulations.

We note that the excitation frequency is above the natural frequency. The car
must have passed through resonance, at a speed of about 18.8 km h^{-1}, to get
there. On the rather oversimplified assumptions we have made, it would be
inadvisable to drive at speeds near resonance for any appreciable time.

5.2.4 Resonance

Mathematically, in any of the above cases, if the exciting frequency is equal to
the natural frequency, the steady state amplitude will be infinite. In fact, this
cannot occur; a mathematical reason is that the steady state will never be reached
- it can be shown from the full solution of the equation of motion (including the
transient) that the amplitude at resonance increases linearly with time. A more
practical reason is that in any real case, non-linear effects will limit the
amplitude (perhaps catastrophically!). Also, in real cases there is dissipation of
energy - damping - which reduces the peak amplitude. This will be discussed in
Chapter 6.

5.2.5 Avoidance of vibration

For vibration to occur, three things are necessary: mass, flexibility and excitation. Since all machines and mechanisms have the first two, they will all have natural frequencies of vibration. Excitation is virtually always present in some form. To avoid unwanted vibrations, it is important to select operating conditions well away from resonant frequencies. Operation can either be below the resonance, in which case a low operating speed and high natural frequencies are needed, or above it, with high speeds and low natural frequencies.

Operation below the natural frequency is often selected for measuring instruments. For example, for seismic excitation with $\omega << \omega_n$, it can easily be shown that the spring extension ($x - x_0$ in the notation of Figure 5.9) is proportional to ω^2, and thus to the acceleration of the support point. This gives a direct way of measuring acceleration.

Operation well above the natural frequency can be used to provide a "fixed" or inertial platform. So long as $\omega >> \omega_n$, the "absolute" motion of the mass is very small, and it is effectively isolated from movement of the support point. Vehicle suspensions aim to do this - they provide a smooth ride independent of roughness in the road. Seismographs, used for measuring earthquakes, also work in this mode. Frequencies associated with earthquakes are, however, so low (a few Hz) that extremely low values of ω_n must be used.

When a machine operates above its natural frequency, it will generally have to accelerate up through the resonant condition, and it is important to make sure that this happens quickly. Most machines have several natural frequencies, and it may not be practical to operate above all of them. In such cases, an operating speed which lies in a reasonably wide gap between natural frequencies must be chosen. Common examples of machines operating above some of their natural frequencies are domestic spin driers and vacuum cleaners, whose resonances can be detected as a temporary increase in noise or vibration as the machine runs up to speed.

It may not always be possible to select operating speeds independently of other factors. For example, synchronous electrical machines must run at a speed directly related to the electrical frequency. In such cases we have to control vibration by either adjusting the natural frequencies, minimising the excitation or introducing damping.

Natural frequencies can only be adjusted by changing the mass or stiffness. Increasing mass will reduce natural frequency, while increasing stiffness will increase it.

Minimising excitation can be done by improved balancing and by various vibration isolation techniques which are beyond the scope of this book. The concept of damping will be covered in the next chapter.

EXAMPLES

5.1   A vehicle suspension has a natural frequency of 1 Hz. What will be the natural frequency if (a) a load is added which increases the all-up mass by 50%; (b) the springs are doubled in length, but otherwise not altered; (c) a second identical spring is added in parallel to each of the existing ones ?
(Ans: (a) 0.81 Hz, (b) 0.71 Hz, (c) 1.41 Hz)

5.2   The hook of a spring balance moves 10 mm when a load is hung on it. What will be its natural frequency of vibration?
(Ans: 4.98 Hz)

5.3   A pendulum clock loses 1 minute a day. The period of the pendulum should be 2 s. What change in pendulum length should be made?
(Ans: shorten by 1.4 mm)

5.4   The cage and load of a lift have a total mass of 950 kg. The lift is suspended by a wire which extends under load by 0.1 mm per kN for each metre of its length. Calculate the frequency of oscillations of the lift when it stops at the ground floor (supported on 20 m of wire) and at the fifth floor (5 m of wire)
(Ans: 3.65 Hz, 7.30 Hz)

5.5   A machine of mass 200 kg is mounted on a bed which deflects 1 mm under the load. When the machine runs at 500 rev min^{-1} it produces a fluctuating vertical force of 500 N. What will be the amplitude of vibration of the machine?
(Ans: 0.35 mm)

5.6   A machine stands on spring supports which are not fixed to the floor. The machine vibrates at 20 Hz. What is the maximum amplitude of vibration if the supports are not to leave the floor?
(Ans: 0.62 mm)

5.7   A vehicle of mass 1 tonne and with suspension stiffness of 40 kN m^{-1} travels at 50 km h^{-1} along a road whose surface undulates with a wavelength of 15 m and an amplitude of 20 mm. What is the amplitude of motion of the car body?

(Ans: 130 mm)

BIBLIOGRAPHY

Collinson CD, *Introductory Mechanics*. Edward Arnold, 1980 (Chapter 4)

Meriam JL, *Dynamics*, Wiley, 1980 (Chapter 4)

6

Work and Energy

In the last chapter, we mentioned dissipation of energy. Here, we will consider the nature and properties of energy and, in particular, the circumstances under which it is conserved or lost.

6.1 CONSERVATION OF ENERGY

The definition of Newton's Second Law in Chapter 2 and its use for deriving equations of motion in Chapters 4 and 5 are not the only possible formulations. Others may be obtained by slight changes of structure.

As an example, let us look at the equation of motion for a forced vibration situation, such as those considered in Section 5.2 but including a gravitational term:

$$m\ddot{x} + kx + mg = \mathbf{F}(t)$$

(where $\mathbf{F}(t)$ is the forcing function, which is time dependent, and the coordinate x has its origin at the unstretched position of the spring and is positive upwards). If we integrate this equation with respect to position, using the substitution $dx = \dot{x}dt$ to integrate the acceleration term, we obtain:

$$\int m\ddot{x}\dot{x}\,dt + \int kx\,dx + \int mg\,dx = \int F\,dx$$

$$\tfrac{1}{2}m\dot{x}^2 + \tfrac{1}{2}kx^2 + mgx = \int F(x)\,dx + \text{const}$$

where **F** is now considered as a function of position rather than time.

The three terms on the left hand side of this equation can be considered as different ways of storing energy in a system. The first, associated with the velocity of the mass, is called *kinetic energy*. The second, associated with the spring, is called *strain energy*, and the third is *gravitational potential energy*. The energy stored by these methods is *recoverable*: if the process which put the energy in is reversed, the energy will come out again. Such a process is termed *reversible*.

These three are not the only forms in which energy can appear - there are also thermal, electrical and other forms - but they are the main ones which are relevant in mechanics. As a group, they are called *mechanical energy*. The zero point of mechanical energy is arbitrary; choosing a different height datum, for example, would only add constant terms into the equation, and these could be merged with the constant of integration. The quantity of interest in mechanics is the *change* in energy, or the redistribution of it between the different forms.

The term on the right hand side is called the *work* done by the force **F**. Putting the equation in words: 'the change in total mechanical energy of a system is equal to the work done on the system by external forces'. In this form, it applies to all systems, not just the mass/spring system used as an example here.

The units of work and energy (which must obviously be the same) are *newton-metres* (N m), given the special name *joules* (J). Work and energy are scalars - they have no directional information associated with them. In vector terms, work is the scalar product of the force and distance vectors.

In the particular case of free vibration, the force **F** is zero. The sum of the three forms of energy is then constant. As the mass moves, energy is converted from one form to another; later in the cycle it is converted back again. But none is lost. The energy of the system is *conserved*. A system for which this is true is called a *conservative* system. If **F** varies harmonically, then as we saw in Section 5.2.1, under steady state conditions both position and force vary as $\cos \omega t$. The term on the right hand side then integrates to zero over any whole number of cycles of oscillation, and the forced vibration system is conservative when in steady state. In other words, no external energy is required to maintain it.

The energy conservation method can be used to solve many problems as an alternative to the equation of motion method. This is best illustrated by a few examples.

Example 1

A mass m oscillates on a spring k. Calculate the natural frequency.

Let us leave out gravitational effects. The sum of kinetic energy (KE) and strain energy (SE) is constant. The minimum KE is zero when the SE is maximum at the end of the cycle, when velocity = 0, and the minimum SE is zero when the KE is maximum at the centre of the cycle, when displacement = 0. The maximum KE is therefore equal to the maximum SE. Assuming that $x = X\cos\omega_n t$:

$$\text{maximum displacement} = X; \quad \text{maximum velocity} = \omega_n X$$

$$KE_{max} = \tfrac{1}{2}m(\omega_n X)^2$$

$$= SE_{max} = \tfrac{1}{2}kX^2$$

$$\therefore \omega_n^2 = \frac{k}{m}$$

Example 2

A catapult fires a stone of mass 25 g vertically upwards. The elastic has a stiffness of 400 N m^{-1}, and is stretched by 10 cm at the moment of release. What height does the stone reach?

The initial strain energy in the elastic must equal the final gravitational potential energy of the stone, relative to a datum at the launch height:

$$\tfrac{1}{2}kx^2 = \tfrac{1}{2}\times400\times0.1^2 = mgh = 0.025\times9.81\times h$$

$$\therefore h = 8.15 \text{ m}$$

Example 3

A roller-coaster car starts from rest at the top of a slope of 45° to the horizontal. How fast will it be moving when it has travelled 35 m?

The initial potential energy must equal the final kinetic energy, relative to a datum at the end point required. When it has travelled 35 m, it will have descended $35/\sqrt{2}$ m.

$$\tfrac{1}{2}mv^2 = mgh = m \times 9.81 \times 35/\sqrt{2}$$

$$\therefore v = 22.0 \text{ m/s}$$

Energy methods obviously lead to particularly simple solutions for problems of this type, involving conservative systems with no external forces. They also offer a very powerful approach for obtaining solutions to non-linear problems which are intractable by other methods, and a sound basis for obtaining approximate solutions in even more complex cases.

6.2 WORK

The change in total mechanical energy of a system is equal to the work done on the system by external forces. It is important to distinguish clearly between work done *on* a system and work done *by* it. The two are equal in magnitude, but opposite in sign.

Work is calculated by integrating a force over a distance *in the direction of action of the force*. Force and distance are both vectors: work is their scalar product:

$$W = \int \mathbf{F}.d\mathbf{x}$$

If there is no component of force in the direction of motion, no work is done. The scalar product of two perpendicular vectors is zero.

All three forms of energy we identified above can in fact be considered in terms of work:

Kinetic: $F = m\ddot{x}$ $\displaystyle \int F dx = m \int \ddot{x} dx = m \int \ddot{x}\dot{x} dt = \tfrac{1}{2}m\dot{x}^2$

Strain: $F = kx$ $\displaystyle \int F dx = k \int x dx = \tfrac{1}{2}kx^2$

Potential: $F = mg$ $\displaystyle \int F dx = mg \int dx = mgx$

Relationships such as these allow us to calculate the work/energy involved in other processes. For example, a non-linear spring might have a characteristic:

$$F = \alpha x^2$$

where α is a constant. The strain energy stored in such a spring is found by calculating the work done to deform it:

$$SE = \int F dx = \alpha \int x^2 dx = \tfrac{1}{3}\alpha x^3$$

6.3 POWER

The rate of change of energy, or the rate of doing work, is called *power*. The units of power are *joules per second* (J s^{-1}) or *watts* (W). It is the power of an energy transmission system, such as an electrical transmission line or a gearbox, or conversion system, such as an engine or electric motor, which is the main determining factor in its size and cost. A larger system is usually called upon not just to deliver more energy than a smaller, but to do so more rapidly - it is more powerful.

In mechanics, it is very common to evaluate power as the rate of doing work. Since work is given by force × distance (or the equivalent integral), power is force × distance/time = force × speed (or the integral of force with respect to speed). As with work, power is a scalar.

Examples

A vehicle of mass 1000 kg accelerates from rest to 100 km h^{-1} in 10 s. What power (assumed constant over the time period) is required?

Since the power is constant, it must be equal to the final kinetic energy divided by the time (neglecting any restraining forces acting). This is:

$$\frac{\tfrac{1}{2}mv^2}{t} = \frac{\tfrac{1}{2}\times 1000 \times (\dfrac{100\times 1000}{3600})^2}{10} = 38\ 580\ W \quad (38.58\ kW)$$

The assumption of constant power is not very realistic for practical power sources. An alternative assumption might be constant force, and thus constant acceleration. The power will then increase from zero at the start to a maximum at the end. The required constant force is $F = m\ddot{x} = mv/t$, and the maximum power is $Fv = mv^2/t = 77.16$ kW - exactly twice the above value. It would also be possible to make other assumptions about how the power or force varies with time.

6.4 CONSERVATIVE AND NON-CONSERVATIVE FORCES

We saw above that for forced vibration, energy is conserved over a whole cycle so long as the forcing function is harmonic. Such a force, where the total work done in going round a closed cycle is zero is described as a *conservative* force. A force where net work is done in going round a closed cycle is *non-conservative*.

Examples of conservative forces are:

- Gravity: any work done (energy gained) in moving upwards is recovered (energy lost) in moving downwards. Moving horizontally does no work.
- Spring forces: strain energy stored when a perfect spring is compressed is recovered when the spring is allowed to extend again.
- Electromagnetic effects not involving electrical resistance: energy can be stored in a capacitor or inductor.

If the energy change in going round a closed path is zero, then so will the energy change in going round it in the other direction be zero. It follows that the energy change involved in going from one point A on the path to another point B is the same whichever way round the path we go. This can be generalized: under the action of conservative forces, the energy change in going from A to B is a function only of the positions of A and B, and independent of the route taken. It is this characteristic that allows the definition of different types of energy storage which we saw in Section 6.1.

Examples of non-conservative forces are:

- Solid Friction: friction forces always oppose the motion. Whatever the direction of motion, the force is in the opposite direction and work is always done.
- Fluid Friction (viscosity): this is similar to solid friction, except that its magnitude depends more strongly on velocity.
- Electro-magnetic effects involving electrical resistance.
- Internal or *hysteresis* effects which occur when materials are taken through a stress cycle.

Non-conservative forces are also known as *dissipative forces* - they always lead to a loss or dissipation of mechanical energy from a system. The energy is usually converted to heat. Although some of it could conceivably be converted back to mechanical energy, this is the realm of thermodynamics, not mechanics. It is not possible to define an energy type associated with dissipative forces, since the work done in getting from A to B depends on the route taken. The work cannot be recovered by reversing the direction of motion. The actions of such forces are *irreversible*.

Solid friction occurs when two dry solid materials move against each other. Fluid friction occurs when there is a layer of fluid (usually a lubricating liquid such as oil) between them, or when a body moves through a fluid such as water or air. Electromagnetic forces occur when a current-carrying conductor (with electrical resistance) moves in a magnetic field. Hysteresis effects arise when materials are deformed and relaxed again. For real materials, this usually involves some energy loss. In all these cases, dissipative forces are generated, which must be included in equations of motion (or, alternatively, work is done which must be included in the energy balance of a system).

6.4.1 Solid friction

Solid friction, otherwise known as *dry sliding friction*, arises from inter-molecular forces in the two bodies concerned. The net effect is to produce a tangential force at the interface between the bodies, in such a direction as to oppose the relative motion.

The simplest model of dry sliding friction is the Coulomb model. This states that if there is a perpendicular force R between two surfaces, the friction force F between the surfaces will be less than or equal to μR, where μ is an experimental constant called the coefficient of friction (see Figure 6.1).

F acts tangentially to the surfaces, and is of such magnitude and direction as to prevent motion if possible, or to reduce it to a minimum. If another force P is applied to the body in the direction of the interface, F will be equal to P, and opposite to it in direction, so long as $P < \mu R$. If P is greater than μR, then F will equal μR, and the body will accelerate under the net force $(P - F)$.

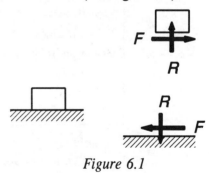

Figure 6.1

As an example, consider a rectangular block of weight W on an inclined plane surface at angle α to the horizontal, with a friction coefficient μ between the block and the plane (Figure 6.2).

Referring to the free body diagram at the top, the weight W has a component $W\sin\alpha$ down the plane, so that the friction force F must be up the plane, as shown. The normal reaction force $R = W\cos\alpha$ (by equilibrium perpendicular to the plane). If $W\sin\alpha < \mu R$, the friction force will just balance the weight component, and the block will not move. If $W\sin\alpha > \mu R$, however, the friction force will be inadequate to prevent motion, and the block will accelerate down the plane under a force $(W\sin\alpha - \mu R)$. This leads to an alternative formulation of the friction coefficient: the *angle of friction* λ is defined as the angle of a plane such that the block will just slide down. It follows that $W\sin\lambda = \mu R = \mu W\cos\lambda$, or $\tan\lambda = \mu$.

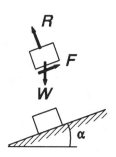

Figure 6.2

The actual value of the coefficient of friction is strongly dependent on the nature of the surfaces involved, their surface finish, and other factors such as temperature. Some typical values are given in Table 6.1.

Materials	μ
Steel/Steel	0.8
Steel/Brass	0.35
Steel/Hard Wood	0.2 - 0.6
Steel/PTFE	0.04
Steel/Nylon	0.3 - 0.5
Steel/Rubber	0.6 - 0.9
Brake lining/Cast Iron	0.35 - 0.5
Brake pad/Cast Iron	0.3
Wood/Wood	0.25 - 0.5
Rubber/Asphalt	0.5 - 0.8
Aluminium/Aluminium	1.35

Table 6.1: Typical coefficients of dry sliding friction for various pairs of materials

Because of the inequality, Coulomb friction leads to equations having no unique solution, and to discontinuities in behaviour. For example, if the angle of the plane in Figure 6.2 is greater than λ, an external force of $W(\sin\alpha - \mu\cos\alpha)$ up the plane will be needed to stop the block sliding down. But a much larger force $W(\sin\alpha + \mu\cos\alpha)$ would be needed to push it up the plane, since the friction force would then be acting downwards. Similarly, if a body on a horizontal surface is subject to spring and friction forces (Figure 6.3), it can be in equilibrium in any position from $x = -\mu R/k$ to $x = +\mu R/k$. These features, combined with the wide ranges of uncertainty on friction coefficients, make it

difficult to incorporate dry friction in analytical
models.

A further problem is that we have assumed that
the maximum value of the coefficient of friction -
the *limiting* value (which applies when motion is just
about to start) - is the same as the value that applies
once there is relative motion - the *dynamic* value.
This is not usually the case; the dynamic coefficient
of friction is often significantly lower (a few percent

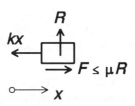

Figure 6.3

to a factor of 2) than the limiting coefficient. This leads to *stick-slip* behaviour.
It is common experience that things often start to move with a jerk, and if
allowed to stop, may be difficult to start again. This phenomenon is responsible
for the creaking of unlubricated hinges, the squeaking of chair legs when
dragged across a solid floor, etc.

6.4.2 Fluid friction

Fluid friction arises from momentum transfers within a flowing fluid. Under
some conditions, the transfers happen at the molecular level, and the flow is
described as *laminar*. Under other conditions, the transfers are of larger
elements of fluid, and the flow is said to be *turbulent*. Calculation of the forces
and energies involved is in the realm of fluid mechanics. Here we will just
consider overall effects.

Laminar flow occurs at low speeds and on small scales. Forces are
proportional to velocity and to a fluid property called *viscosity*. Examples are
most cases of oil lubrication (with a highly viscous fluid flowing relatively
slowly in a narrow passage) and the flow in
dashpots or *viscous dampers*. These consist of a
reservoir of fluid in which is a close-fitting piston
(Figure 6.4). When the piston is moved, fluid flows
from one side of it to the other either through the
clearance round the edge, or through a hole drilled
in it. The flow is laminar, and the force necessary
to move the piston is proportional to its velocity.
Such devices are used on automatic door closing
systems, vehicle suspensions and in some designs of
carburetter. Their function is to apply a temporary
force when transient loads are encountered.

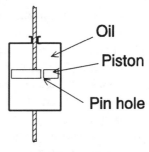

Figure 6.4

Since viscous forces are proportional to
velocity, the extra terms in equations are linear, and the equations are amenable
to analytic solution. For this reason, it is often assumed that fluid forces are of
this type, even when this may not strictly be the case.

Turbulent fluid flow occurs at higher speeds and larger sizes, and with less viscous fluids. The most common cases (from the point of view of mechanics) are when a solid body moves through a fluid such as air or water. A drag force opposing the motion appears, which is approximately proportional to velocity squared. (Under some conditions, a lift force, perpendicular to the motion, also appears. Because it is perpendicular to the motion, the lift force is of course non-dissipative.) A square law (non-linear) term causes problems in analysis, and only the simplest turbulent drag cases are easily solved analytically.

6.4.3 Electromagnetic forces

When a conductor moves in a magnetic field, a current is induced in it which is proportional to velocity. If there is a closed circuit and the conductor has resistance, energy is dissipated at a rate proportional to current, and thus velocity, squared. This energy must have come from the mechanical force needed to move the conductor. Rate of energy dissipation (power) is force times velocity, so that the force needed to move the conductor must be proportional to velocity.

Such a system is called *eddy current damping*, and is widely used to suppress oscillations in measuring instruments. An aluminium armature is fixed to the moving part of the instrument, and moves between the poles of a permanent magnet. Forces are produced which oppose high velocity movements of the armature.

Conveniently, this system is also linear, and has the same characteristics as a viscous fluid system.

6.4.4 Hysteresis losses

When a material is taken through a load cycle, there is often of net loss of energy due to internal irreversibilities in the material. This is known as *hysteresis* or *internal damping*. For materials designed for cyclic loading and deflection, such as spring steels, it is usually very small. For some other materials, particularly composites such as glass reinforced plastics and steel reinforced concrete, it can be large. Such properties can be put to good use for sound or vibration absorption purposes. Experimentally, the energy dissipated per cycle is roughly independent of frequency and proportional to the square of amplitude. This is not a particularly simple model to analyse in detail; if internal damping needs to be taken into account, a linearized model may be used.

6.5 DAMPED FREE VIBRATION

We are now in a position to look at how dissipative forces, or *damping* affect the vibration of a simple oscillator as considered in Chapter 5. We will confine ourselves to linear systems for two reasons: firstly, these are of practical interest since viscous fluid and electromagnetic eddy current dampers are linear, and secondly, because analytic solutions exist, which is not the case for most non-linear systems.

Consider the situation in Figure 6.5: a mass moves under the influence of a linear spring and a linear damper, drawn as a stylized dashpot. Such a system is very similar in principle (though rather different in layout) to a vehicle suspension system. In Figure 6.5, c is the damping coefficient - the ratio of force to velocity - and x is measured from the equilibrium position, so that we may omit the gravity term as previously. The free body diagram for the mass may be used to obtain the equation of motion, as before:

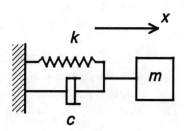

Figure 6.5

$$m\ddot{x} + c\dot{x} + kx = 0$$

We look for a solution of the form $x = e^{\lambda t}$, where λ is a constant, and write $\omega_n^2 = k/m$ as before (ω_n is now called the *undamped* natural frequency), and $\xi = c/2m\omega_n$. Substituting these, we obtain:

$$\lambda^2 e^{\lambda t} + 2\lambda\xi\omega_n e^{\lambda t} + \omega_n^2 e^{\lambda t} = 0$$

$$\text{or} \quad \lambda^2 + 2\lambda\xi\omega_n + \omega_n^2 = 0$$

This equation (the *auxiliary* or *characteristic* equation) is quadratic in λ, and has two solutions, given by:

$$\lambda = \omega_n(-\xi \pm \sqrt{\xi^2 - 1})$$

We denote the two solutions by λ_1 and λ_2. There are thus two corresponding solutions to the equation of motion. Since the latter is linear, any multiple of either solution is also a solution. The general solution (with two arbitrary constants) is then:

$$x = Ae^{\lambda_1 t} + Be^{\lambda_2 t}$$

There are three cases to consider:

1. If $\xi < 1$, λ_1 and λ_2 will be complex. Since complex exponentials can be written in terms of trigonometrical functions, this can be written in the form:

$$x = e^{-\xi\omega_n t}(X\sin(\omega_n t\sqrt{1 - \xi^2} + \phi))$$

where X and ϕ are the "arbitrary" constants. Clearly there are alternative ways of writing this, as for free vibrations, which are the limiting case when $\xi = 0$. Mathematically, it is possible for ξ to be less than zero, but this is not relevant physically in our context of energy dissipation.

2. If $\xi > 1$, both λ_1 and λ_2 will be real. The solution can then be written:

$$x = e^{-\xi\omega_n t}(Ae^{\omega t} + Be^{-\omega t})$$

$$\text{where} \quad \omega = \omega_n\sqrt{\xi^2 - 1}$$

and A and B are "arbitrary" constants evaluated from the initial or other specified conditions. This solution may also be written in terms of hyperbolic functions.

3. If $\xi = 1$, λ_1 will be equal to λ_2, and we must seek another solution. The complete solution turns out to be:

$$x = e^{-\omega_n t}(C + Dt)$$

with C and D coming from initial conditions.

The first case is clearly an oscillatory solution - it contains a sinusoidal term - but the maximum amplitude decreases exponentially with time. Such motion is described as *underdamped*. The second case is not oscillatory, but decays as the sum of two exponentials. The oscillations are completely suppressed by the damping. The motion is *overdamped*. The third case is the boundary between the two - the motion is an exponential decay. It is *critically damped*. These terms lead to the name *critical damping ratio* for the quantity ξ.

6.5.1 Overdamped motion

A typical displacement/time graph for an overdamped system is shown in Figure 6.6. The actual numerical values adopted here are: $\xi = 1.3$, $A = 10$, $B = -8$. The upper broken line represents the first 'A' exponential term, and the lower

one the second '*B*' term. The solid line
is the overall effect.

The motion is not oscillatory,
although it is possible for the trajectory
to cross the axis once if the initial
velocity is towards the axis and
sufficiently high.

Overdamping is not normally used
deliberately in systems which are
primarily dynamic, although it may
occur in systems where the dynamics is
secondary to the some other function.

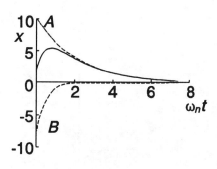

Figure 6.6

6.5.2 Critically Damped Motion

Figure 6.7 shows some examples of motion in a critically damped system. The
detail depends, of course, on the values
of C and D, or equivalently on the
initial conditions. Curve 1 shows the
path when the mass is released from
rest, curve 2 that when the mass is
released with an initial velocity away
from the equilibrium position, and
curve 3 that when the initial velocity is
towards equilibrium. Although in the
latter case, as for overdamping, the
path may cross the axis once, the
motion is not oscillatory.

Critical damping is often used on
measuring instruments such as
electrical meters. Its particular virtue is

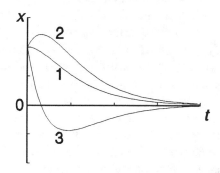

Figure 6.7

that the moving part returns towards the equilibrium position at the maximum
possible rate, without oscillation. It is also used as target state in many other
applications, such as vehicle suspensions. It is rarely achieved precisely in such
situations because the load (mass) may vary without corresponding changes in
the stiffness and damping coefficient; this changes the critical damping ratio.

6.5.3 Underdamped motion

Figure 6.8 shows an underdamped oscillation; this particular one is for $\xi = 0.17$
and $\phi = 0$. The broken lines top and bottom show the exponential decay
envelopes of the oscillatory motion, whose equations are $x = \pm X e^{-\xi \omega_n t}$. The
natural frequency of the system is:

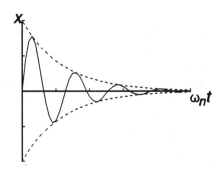

Figure 6.8

$$\omega_d = \omega_n\sqrt{1 - \xi^2}$$

This is the *damped* natural frequency, and is clearly smaller than ω_n, the undamped natural frequency. For light damping, however, the two do not differ much: the reduction is about 1% for $\xi = 0.14$, and less than 5% at $\xi = 0.3$. Typical values of ξ for "stray" damping (arising from air resistance, friction, hysteresis, etc) are often in this kind of region, and it may be acceptable to assume that the frequencies are the same. In the limit of critical damping, the frequency becomes zero, the period infinite.

All real free vibrations are underdamped due to the existence of various dissipative forces, as discussed in Chapter 5. Underdamping may also be deliberately chosen for instruments in preference to critical damping, as the speed of response is improved. Consider, for example, a critically damped system starting from rest and displacement X_0 at time zero: the displacement will be 1% of X_0 when $\omega_n t = 6.64$. For the same initial conditions and a critical damping ratio of 0.83, the first (negative going) peak will be 1% of X_0, and will occur at about $\omega_n t = 5.58$. Although the motion is oscillatory, it falls to within any specified amplitude range more quickly than the critically damped case.

6.5.4 Logarithmic decrement

The successive positive peaks on the underdamped oscillation curve (Figure 6.8) occur at intervals of 2π in $\omega_d t$ (with the negative peaks half way between). We can obtain the height X_n of the nth peak by substituting $\omega_d t = 2\pi n$ in the position equation:

$$X_n = X \exp \left[\frac{-2\pi n \xi}{\sqrt{1 - \xi^2}} \right]$$

(which assumes we have selected our origin to make $\phi = 0$.) Further, we can obtain the ratio of the heights of the n th and m th peaks ($m > n$):

$$\frac{X_n}{X_m} = \exp \left[\frac{2\pi (m - n) \xi}{\sqrt{1 - \xi^2}} \right]$$

This gives a simple and direct way of measuring the critical damping ratio ξ. We measure the heights of any two peaks, and calculate the *logarithmic decrement*:

$$d = \frac{1}{m - n} \ln \frac{X_n}{X_m}$$

The logarithmic decrement (or log dec) is simply the ratio of any two successive positive (or negative) peak heights. There is no need to know n and m separately; we just need to know their difference, which is the number of complete cycles between the two measured peaks. If one of the peaks is positive and the other negative, we need half the number of half-cycles between them (e.g. 2.5 or 12.5). The critical damping ratio is then:

$$\xi = \frac{d}{\sqrt{4\pi^2 + d^2}}$$

For light damping ($\xi^2 \ll 1$), $\xi \approx d/2\pi$. This is accurate to 10% up to about $\xi = 0.4$.

Example

An oscillation is observed to decay to 50% of its original amplitude after 10 cycles. Calculate the critical damping ratio.

$$d = \frac{1}{10}\ln 2 = 0.0693$$

$$\therefore \ \xi = \frac{d}{\sqrt{4\pi^2 + d^2}} = 0.011$$

In this case, the approximate value $\xi = d/2\pi$ would have been perfectly satisfactory.

6.6 DAMPED FORCED VIBRATION

The most general case of vibration is the combination of the forced vibration case considered in Section 5.2 and the damped vibration case of Section 6.5. The equation of motion of such a system (with linear damping and harmonic excitation) is:

$$m\ddot{x} + c\dot{x} + kx = F_0\cos(\omega t)$$

The solution of this equation follows similar lines to that for undamped forced vibration (Section 5.2.1). It consists of the sum of a transient solution (complementary function), which is the same as for free damped vibration Section 6.5, and a steady state solution (particular integral). This time the transient is correctly named: we actually have dissipative terms in the equation, and do not have to invoke arguments about "in reality" to remove it from the long-term solution. The steady state solution is again found by the use of an exponential or trigonometric substitution. The algebra is straightforward, though somewhat laborious. The steady-state solution for the case of direct or seismic excitation is:

$$x = X\cos(\omega t - \phi)$$

where:

$$\frac{X}{X_0} = \left[\left(1 - \left(\frac{\omega}{\omega_n} \right)^2 \right)^2 + \left(2\xi \frac{\omega}{\omega_n} \right)^2 \right]^{-0.5}$$

$$\tan \phi = \frac{2\xi \frac{\omega}{\omega_n}}{1 - \left(\frac{\omega}{\omega_n} \right)^2}$$

and:$$\quad X_0 = \frac{F_0}{m} \qquad \omega_n = \sqrt{\frac{k}{m}} \qquad \xi = \frac{c}{2\sqrt{mk}}$$

It can be seen that the steady state motion is sinusoidal, with amplitude depending on both the critical damping ratio and on the ratio between the forcing and the undamped natural frequencies. There is also a phase shift between the forcing frequency and the response which varies from zero at low frequencies, through 90° at the undamped natural frequency to 180° at very high frequencies.

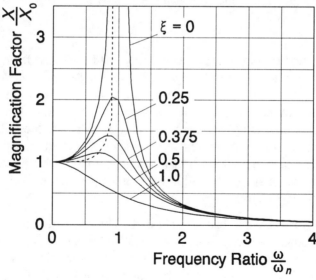

Figure 6.9

Figure 6.9 shows the magnification ratio X/X_0 for various critical damping ratios. It can be seen that for the lower critical damping ratios, there is a resonance peak whose height falls as the damping increases. It is quite easily shown that the peak disappears entirely at $\xi = 1/\sqrt{2} \simeq 0.707$, after which there is no resonance in amplitude, though there is still a phase change. The resonant frequency falls as the damping increases; the dashed line in Figure 6.9 shows the locus of the peaks on the resonance curves. The resonant frequency ω_r is **not** the same as the damped natural frequency ω_d:

$$\text{undamped natural frequency} = \omega_n$$
$$\text{damped natural frequency } \omega_d = \omega_n\sqrt{1 - \xi^2}$$
$$\text{damped resonant frequency } \omega_r = \omega_n\sqrt{1 - 2\xi^2}$$

EXAMPLES

6.1   A magnet is found to exert a force of 1 N on a steel ball of diameter 10 mm and mass 4 gm with its centre a distance 50 mm from the end of the magnet. When it is 100 mm away, the force is 0.3 N. At what speed will it hit the magnet if released from rest at this distance? (Neglect air resistance and assume the ball does not rotate. Hint: use an energy method and remember that the effective centre of the magnet will not be at its end.)
(Ans: 10.1 m s^{-1})

6.2   A fairground ride involves a car of mass 700 kg starting from rest at the top of a straight slope of angle 45° and accelerating down it under gravity. It then enters (through a short transition section) the bottom of a vertical circular track 20 m in diameter, and 'loops the loop' inside the track. By considering the energy of the car, calculate the initial release height necessary for it to remain in contact with the circular track all the way round (a) ignoring frictional and other losses, and (b) assuming a constant frictional force of 400 N acting against the motion.
(Ans: 25 m, 29.2 m)

6.3   A clockwork toy car has a mass of 0.1 kg. It is driven by a spring which produces an initial force of 1 N. The force then falls linearly with distance travelled, becoming zero after 3 m. Thereafter, the spring has no effect. There is a constant frictional force of 0.1 N opposing the motion. The spring is fully wound and the car is released from rest. Calculate how far it travels before stopping.
(Ans: 15 m)

6.4   A meteorite falling straight towards the sun from an infinite distance falls down a vertical mine shaft on the equator without touching the sides. What time is it? (Hint: consider the orbital velocity of the earth and the potential, relative to the sun, and kinetic energies of the meteorite.)

(Ans: about 2:25 am)

6.5 Water flows over a weir 2 m high at a rate of 30 m^3 s^{-1}. Approximately what is the maximum power which could be extracted from the flow?

(Ans: 590 kW)

6.6 A machine part of effective mass 100 kg is moving freely at 7 m s^{-1} when it comes into contact with a viscous damper which exerts a retarding force $F = 1.7 v$, where v is the instantaneous velocity in m s^{-1} and F is in kN. Calculate how fast the part is moving when it has travelled a further 0.2 m and 0.4 m. How much energy has been dissipated in the latter case?

(Ans: 3.6 m s^{-1}, 0.2 m s^{-1}, 2448 J)

6.7 Show that, for damping less than 10% of critical, the frequency of free vibrations of a mass/spring/damper system is within 1% of the undamped natural frequency. How much is it affected by damping which is 90% of critical?

(Ans: reduced to 44%)

6.8 A body of mass 10 g is suspended by a spring of stiffness 0.25 N m^{-1} and subject to damping which is 1% of critical. After approximately how many oscillations will the amplitude of vibration have halved? How long will this take?

(Ans: 11, 13.8 s)

6.9 A body of mass 10 kg is supported on a system which has a damping of 100 N s m^{-1}. What is the maximum support spring stiffness, if oscillations are not to be possible? What will be the natural frequency of oscillation if the spring is twice this stiffness?

(Ans: 250 N m^{-1}, 0.796 Hz)

BIBLIOGRAPHY

Smith RC and Smith P, *Mechanics*. Wiley, 1971 (Chapter 5)
Meriam JL, *Dynamics*. Wiley, 1980 (Chapter 3)
Prentis J, *Engineering Mechanics*. Oxford, 1979 (Chapter 6)

7

Momentum

The energy equations of the last chapter involve the taking of scalar products, thus losing the vector information carried by forces and velocities. In this chapter we will look at an alternative integration of Newton's second law which preserves the vector information.

7.1 CONSERVATION AND CHANGE OF MOMENTUM

We may integrate Newton's second law with respect to time:

$$\int \mathbf{F}\,dt = \int m\ddot{x}\,dt = m\mathbf{v} + \text{const}$$

The group $m\mathbf{v}$ is called *momentum*, and is a vector quantity.

This form of the law applies to a *system* enclosed by a *control surface*. A system is any identified group of bodies which may be stationary or in motion, and may or may not interact with each other. They are surrounded by a control surface, which is an identified boundary. Part or all of a control surface may coincide with a physical boundary, or it may be purely abstract.

Newton's second law in this form states that the rate of change of the total momentum of the system (or control volume) is equal to the total **external** force which acts on the bodies inside the control surface. **Internal** forces (i.e. forces of interaction between bodies inside the control volume) have no effect on the total momentum. By Newton's third law, they come in equal and opposite pairs, whose effects on the total momentum cancel out. It is only forces which cross the control volume which can affect the momentum within it.

A particular special case is when the external forces are zero. Then the total momentum in the control volume is constant. For example, in Figure 7.1a, the system consists of a wheeled vehicle (assumed frictionless) of mass 10 tonnes (10 000 kg), moving at 2 m s⁻¹, and a stationary body of mass 1 tonne (1000 kg). The control surface is shown dashed. The mass is released (which may require forces to act in the vertical direction) and lands in the vehicle. Horizontal and vertical internal forces will act - friction, impacts, etc - until eventually the vehicle and mass are moving at the same speed v (Figure 7.1b).

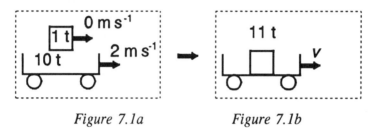

Figure 7.1a   Figure 7.1b

No external forces have acted in the horizontal direction, so the system momentum must be unchanged in that direction. We can thus obtain the speed v:

$$(10\ 000\ +\ 1000)\times v\ =\ (10\ 000)\times 2\ +\ 1000\times 0$$

$$\therefore\ v\ =\ \frac{20\ 000}{11\ 000}\ =\ 1.8\ \text{m s}^{-1}$$

The internal forces (friction, etc) cannot affect the overall momentum, but they can affect the energy. In this case they are dissipative, and energy is lost from the system. Considering only kinetic energy, initially the total is ½(10 000)×2² = 20 000 J. Finally, it is ½(11 000)×1.8² = 18 000 J.

In systems with an energy source, the total energy may increase. For example, a gun and a shell are initially at rest. Chemical energy is released which gives kinetic energy to both gun and shell. But assuming the gun is free to recoil, the final momentum of the system must be zero. Whatever positive momentum is acquired by the shell must be balanced by an equal negative momentum of the gun. If the gun is not free to recoil, an external force must be acting on the system (through the gun mountings), and the total momentum will change. Other ways in which energy may be introduced are electrical and nuclear, or by the release of strain energy (i.e. a spring).

Example

A Champagne bottle is lying on its side on a horizontal surface. It ejects its cork at a relative velocity of 5 m s⁻¹. The mass of the cork is 10 g, and that of the bottle (and contents) is 1.2 kg. What is the initial velocity of the bottle?

Let the required velocity be v. The momentum of the cork is $(5 - v) \times 0.01$ (since the given velocity is relative, not absolute). The momentum of the bottle etc. is $-1.2v$. These must sum to zero, whence $v = 0.04$ m s⁻¹).

7.1.1 Impulse

If an external force acts for a finite time, it produces a finite change in momentum:

$$\int \mathbf{F}\,dt = \text{(final momentum)} - \text{(initial momentum)}$$

The integral is called the *Impulse* of the force. The same change of momentum can be produced by many different force/time histories. A small force may act over a long period, or a large one over a short time. The force need not be constant, but may rise to a maximum and decay again with an arbitrary profile. Figure 7.2 shows some examples of force/time profiles with (approximately) the same impulse.

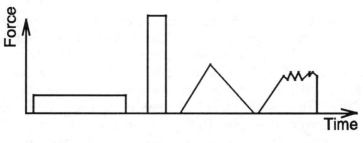

Figure 7.2

The first two profiles show a constant force acting over a fixed time. Such a force might be produced by a hanging weight or by a linear electric motor. The third profile, where the force rises to a maximum and then falls again could be muscle power, while the fourth where it rises, remains roughly constant and then stops abruptly is typical of a rocket or a gun barrel.

Example

A "people mover" train has an all-up mass of 5 tonnes. It is propelled by a linear electric motor, which produces a constant accelerating force of 10 kN. How long does it take to reach its cruising speed of 80 km h⁻¹ ? Ignore friction and air resistance.

The final momentum of the train is:

$$5000 \times \frac{80\ 000}{3600} = 1.11 \times 10^5 \ \text{kg m s}^{-1}$$

This is equal to the impulse of the accelerating force, Ft. $F = 10\ 000$ N, whence $t = 1.11 \times 10^5/10^4 = 11.1$ s.

The limiting case of an infinite force acting for zero time is called an *impulsive force*. It can have an impulse of any value, and is quite a good model for many very rapidly acting forces - e.g. hammer blows. Since the time is zero, finite forces can have no influence, and so can be ignored in the presence of impulsive forces. For example, we can ignore the effect of gravity during the instant that a cricket bat is in contact with the ball, but not before or after that instant.

Example

A pile driver drops a mass of 1 tonne on to the top of a pile of mass 300 kg from a height of 2 m. The pile is subject to a constant resistance force of 100 kN from the ground, while it is moving. How far into the ground is the pile driven?

When dropped from a height of 2 m, the mass will acquire a velocity of 6.264 m s⁻¹ (by acceleration or energy calculation). Its momentum will be 6264 kg m s⁻¹. The impact can be considered to be impulsive, so we can ignore resistance and gravitational effects during it. So, by momentum, the velocity of the mass and pile, now moving as one body, after the impact will be 6264/(1000 + 300) = 4.82 m s⁻¹. They then move under the action of the resisting force and their weight. This is a net upward force of 87.25 kN. The motion is a constant acceleration of 87250/1300 = 67.1 m s⁻² (upwards). The distance travelled before coming to rest is thus 4.82²/(2×67.1) = 0.17 m.

7.2 REBOUND

In the examples above, either the initial or the final relative velocity between the two bodies in the system was zero - they either started separate, and merged, or they split apart from an initial single body. This is not always the case - the two bodies may collide and rebound (Figure 7.3):

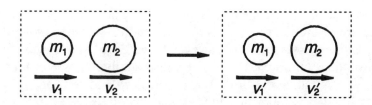

Figure 7.3

If there are no external forces, the momentum equation is:

$$m_1v_1 + m_2v_2 = m_1v_1' + m_2v_2'$$

where the dash indicates the velocity after the collision. If the collision is to occur at all, we know that $v_1 > v_2$, and obviously $v_2' > v_1'$, otherwise they will collide again. But without more information, we cannot calculate the two final velocities.

The extra equation we use comes from experiment. Newton's Law of Restitution states that:

$$v_1' - v_2' = -e(v_1 - v_2)$$

where e, the coefficient of restitution, is a material property which is found to be roughly constant for a given pair of materials over a wide range of relative velocities. The value of e is between 0 and 1.

There are two special cases:

$e = 1$:   The initial and final relative velocities are the same magnitude (though different in sign). This case is known as *perfectly elastic*. Hard, resilient materials such as steel have very high values of e (0.99 or above).

$e = 0$:   The final relative velocity is zero - the two bodies merge. This is the *perfectly inelastic* case. Materials such as putty have this property.

Example

A billiard ball moving at 1 m s^{-1} *collides with an identical stationary ball.
Calculate the final velocities for* $e = 0.9$ *and for* $e = 1$.

We assume that the collision is perfectly symmetrical, so that the final velocities are in the same straight line as the initial velocity. Using the above notation, all the masses are equal, and can be cancelled out. Then $v_1 = 1$ m s^{-1}, $v_2 = 0$; by momentum, $v_1' + v_2' = 1$ m s^{-1}; by restitution, $v_1' - v_2' = -e(1 - 0)$ m^{-1}. If $e = 1$, $v_1' = 0$ and $v_2' = 1$ m s^{-1}. If $e = 0.9$, $v_1' = 0.05$ m s^{-1} and $v_2' = 0.95$ m s^{-1}.

In the first case, the momentum is completely transferred from one ball to the other, and there is no loss of energy. In the second case, the first ball retains some momentum, and there is a loss of energy.

If the two balls were of different masses, the first would retain some momentum, even in a perfectly elastic collision. It can be proved quite generally that there will be no loss of energy for a perfectly elastic collision, whatever the masses and velocities, but there will always be an energy loss if $e < 1$.

If the collision was not symmetrical, there would be no change in the momentum equation for the initial direction of motion, but the two balls would acquire equal and opposite momenta in the perpendicular direction. The restitution equation would not apply in the form given, but could be used along the line joining the centres of the two balls at the moment of contact. Such problems are often best tackled by vector methods.

Example

Newton's Cradle is a toy consisting of a number of identical solid steel balls suspended from a frame such that they are at the same height and, when at rest, are just not in contact with each other.

Consider a three-ball Newton's cradle, as shown in Figure 7.4. The balls are numbered 1, 2, 3 from the left, and are all of mass m. Initially ball 1 is moving with speed 1 unit, the others are stationary. In order to show the behaviour more clearly, we will use a rather unrealistically low coefficient of restitution of 0.8. Initially, $u_1 = 1$, $u_2 = u_3 = 0$. The first collision occurs when 1 hits 2.

Then:

$$mu_1 = mu_1' + mu_2' \qquad \text{(Momentum)}$$

and
$$eu_1 = -(u_1' - u_2') \qquad \text{(Restitution)}$$

from these, $u_1' = 0.1$ and $u_2' = 0.9$

The next thing to happen will be 2 hitting 3, which we can solve in the same manner. But this will slow 2 down, and 1 may hit it again (it does).

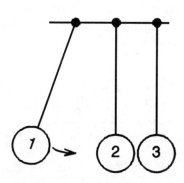

Figure 7.4

We can draw up a state table:

State	Velocity			Energy
	(1)	(2)	(3)	(Units of $\frac{1}{2}mu_i^2$)
Initial	1	0	0	1
After 1 hits 2	0.1	0.9	0	0.82
After 2 hits 3	0.1	0.09	0.81	0.6742
After 1 hits 2 (again)	0.091	0.099	0.81	0.67418

They are now all moving in the same direction with speed increasing from left to right. Nothing more will happen until they swing back. Since they are all simple pendulums of the same length, they will all swing back at the same time. The next state will be:

After swing back	-0.091	-0.099	-0.81
After 3 hits 2	-0.091	-0.729	-0.0081

(2 now hits 1, and the process continues)

EXAMPLES

7.1   Two barges of mass m and $2m$ are connected by a cable of length ℓ. A winch on one of them shortens the cable to half its original length. How far does the heavier barge move?
(Ans: $\ell/6$)

7.2   An astronaut of mass 100 kg holding a spanner of mass 1 kg is outside his ship (which has a mass of 1000 kg) and at rest relative to it. He throws his spanner directly away from the ship at a relative speed of 10 m s⁻¹. When he comes into contact with the ship, he holds on to it.

Calculate the final velocities of all bodies, the intermediate velocity of the astronaut and the change in energy of the system. Where has the energy change gone to/come from?
(Ans: -0.099 m s⁻¹, 9.9 m s⁻¹, -0.009 m s⁻¹, 49.1 J)

7.3   The side of a tent is a rectangle 3 m long and 2 m wide, inclined at an angle of 60° to the vertical. Steady rain falls on the tent at a rate of 0.02 m h⁻¹, and the velocity of the raindrops is 6 m s⁻¹ when they strike the tent. Calculate the force on the tent due to the impact of the raindrops.
        (Ans: 0.17 N)

7.4   A person of mass 78 kg steps off a diving board and hits the water after 1 s. The water exerts a constant retarding force of 4000 N. How long is it before the person comes to rest?
        (Ans: 0.24 s)

7.5   A vehicle of mass 1 tonne is travelling due North at 60 km h⁻¹. It collides with another vehicle of mass 2 tonnes, which is travelling North-East at 50 km h⁻¹, and the two vehicles become interlocked. Calculate the speed and direction of motion immediately after the collision.
        (Ans: 49.6 km h⁻¹, 28.4° E of N)

7.6   A man of mass 80 kg is standing at one end of a boat of mass 120 kg and length 4 m. The other end of the boat is touching the bank. He walks forward and jumps ashore with a relative take-off speed which would carry him 2 m from a fixed position. Determine (a) how far he is from the shore when he jumps, (b) whether he reaches the shore, (c) the speed of the boat immediately after the jump.
        (Ans: 1.6 m, No, 1.25 m s⁻¹)

7.7   A ball is dropped from a height of 10 m. The coefficient of restitution is 0.7. Calculate the height of the 7th rebound.
        (Ans: 6.78 cm)

7.8   Two identical cars of mass 1200 kg are connected by a slack tow rope. One car starts and has attained a speed of 4 m s⁻¹ at the moment the tow rope becomes taut. Assuming a coefficient of restitution of 0.5, calculate the speeds of both cars when the rope again becomes slack. Calculate also the mean tension in the rope, assuming the time interval concerned is 3 s.
        (Ans: 3 m s⁻¹, 1 m s⁻¹, 1200 N)

BIBLIOGRAPHY

Collinson CD, *Introductory Mechanics*. Edward Arnold, 1980 (Chapter 3)
Higginson GR, *Foundations of Engineering Mechanics*. Longman, 1974
  (Chapter 6)

8

Rotation

Many engineering systems consist of or contain rotating elements. Examples are motors, alternators, turbines, fans, compressors, gearboxes. Any material element in a rotating system moves according to Newton's Laws, in the normal fashion. But because all elements are linked together and move in a well defined way relative to each other, it is possible and useful to re-formulate the laws of motion in a way which applies specifically to rotating bodies.

In this book we will, by and large, only consider bodies which are more or less axi-symmetric, and are rotating about their axis of symmetry. This excludes highly unsymmetrical bodies and bodies rotating about more than one axis simultaneously (e.g. spacecraft). The methods developed are, however, readily generalized to more complex cases.

8.1 DEFINITIONS

Angular Velocity:

When a body rotates about an axis, its angular velocity about that axis is the rate of change of the angle between a radial line in the body and a fixed radial line. It is measured in radians per second (rad s^{-1} or often just s^{-1}). The related quantity rotational speed is usually measured in revolutions per minute (rev min^{-1}) or revolutions per second.

Note that an angular velocity is more fundamental than a linear velocity: rotation implies acceleration towards the axis, so that angular velocities should be expressed in absolute terms, not relative. It is possible to tell if you are rotating or not, while it is not possible to tell if you are moving at constant speed in a straight line - it might be the surroundings going the other way.

Angular velocity is a vector, with direction along the axis of rotation. In rotational systems, angular velocity plays the role played by velocity in linear systems. The normal symbol for angular velocity is ω (greek omega), but the symbol $\dot{\theta}$ is also often used. The time derivative of angular velocity is angular acceleration $\dot{\omega}$ or $\ddot{\theta}$.

Moment of a Force:

The (vector) moment **M** of a force **F** about a point O is given by

$$\mathbf{M} = \mathbf{r} \times \mathbf{F}$$

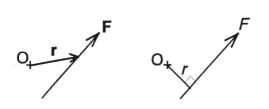

Figure 8.1

where **r** is the position vector of any point on the line of action of **F** relative to O. In scalar terms, $M = rF$, where r is the perpendicular distance from O to the force (see Figure 8.1). In calculating a moment, it is necessary to know and specify both the line of action of the force and the position of the axis. Moment is usually specified in Newton metres (N m).

Couple:

A single force such as that in Figure 8.1 also produces an unbalanced side force on the axis. However, a pair of equal and opposite (parallel) forces such as are shown in Figure 8.2 produce a moment about the axis O without producing an unbalanced force. Such a force system is called a *couple*. The magnitude of a couple is the moment it produces:

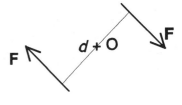

Figure 8.2

$$M = 2\left(F\frac{d}{2}\right) = Fd$$

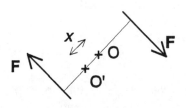

Figure 8.3

If we consider (Figure 8.3) another axis O', parallel to O and a distance x from it, the moment of the couple about O' is:

$$M = F\left(\frac{d}{2} + x\right) + F\left(\frac{d}{2} - x\right) = Fd$$

This is the same as about O; the moment of the couple is independent of the position of the axis. In fact, O' need not even be on the perpendicular to the forces through O - the same moment is obtained for any point.

The same value of moment can obviously be produced by many different pairs of forces, so that the couple is more fundamental than the forces producing it. We often make use of couples without actually considering how they arise. In rotational systems, couple plays the role played by force in linear systems.

Couple is a vector. In a plane (x-y) system, it only has one component (the z component). In three dimensional systems it has three components.

Torque:

Torque is essentially the same as couple, but the term is usually used for the quantity transmitted along a shaft, rather than that applied to it externally. The distinction is similar to that between load and shear force for a beam (see Chapter 10).

8.2 MOTION OF A PARTICLE ABOUT A POINT

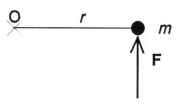

Figure 8.4

The particle m in Figure 8.4 is acted upon by a force F. Its equation of motion is:

$$F = m\ddot{x}$$

But $\dot{x} = r\omega$, where ω is its angular velocity about the point O. Also, the moment of the force F about O is $M = Fr$. So the equation of motion may also be written:

$$M = (mr^2)\dot{\omega} = (mr^2)\ddot{\theta} = I\ddot{\theta}$$

where $I = mr^2$ will be further discussed below.

In a similar fashion, we may calculate the kinetic energy of the particle:

$$E = \frac{1}{2}mv^2 = \frac{1}{2}m(r\omega)^2 = \frac{1}{2}(mr^2)\omega^2 = \frac{1}{2}I\omega^2$$

We may also define the *moment of momentum, h,* (also known as the *angular momentum*) of the particle about point O as the momentum of the particle multiplied by the distance r:

$$h = (mv)r = (mr\omega)r = (mr^2)\omega = I\omega$$

We have thus expressed the basic equations of motion of the particle in terms of angular velocity and acceleration, moment about the point O and the quantity $I = mr^2$. No new principles of mechanics have been introduced - we have just changed our notation.

8.3 SOLID BODIES

The discussion above applies to a single particle. But if we consider several particles which are fixed relative to one another, they have the same angular velocity. We can just sum the equations and consider the moments produced by the forces on the whole system of particles. A solid body is simply an infinite system of particles of this type, so we can write the rotational equation of motion for a solid body as:

$$M = I_o \ddot{\theta}$$

where M is the total moment (couple, torque) applied to the solid body, and:

$$I_o = \int_M r^2 dm$$

is called the *Moment of Inertia* of the body about the axis of rotation O.

All the various kinematic and dynamic equations in linear motion have equivalents for rotational motion, with the substitution of moment for force, angular velocity (acceleration) for linear velocity (acceleration), angular momentum for linear momentum and moment of inertia for mass (notice that there is no special rotational kinetic energy - it is the same in both systems):

Equation	Linear	Rotational
Mass/Acceleration	$F = m\ddot{x}$	$M = I\ddot{\theta}$
Rate of Change of Momentum	$F = d(mv)/dt$	$M = d(I\omega)/dt$
Kinetic Energy	$E = \frac{1}{2}mv^2$	$E = \frac{1}{2}I\omega^2$
Constant Acceleration	$\ddot{x} = \ddot{x}_0 + \dddot{x}t$	$\ddot{\theta} = \ddot{\theta}_0 + \dddot{\theta}t$
	$x = \dot{x}_0 t + \frac{1}{2}\ddot{x}t^2$	$\theta = \dot{\theta}_0 t + \frac{1}{2}\ddot{\theta}t^2$

etc.

Example: The Torsion Pendulum

A torsion pendulum consists of a steel wire 1 m long and 1 mm diameter rigidly fixed at its upper end, supporting a solid aluminium cylinder 10 cm long and 10 cm diameter fixed coaxially at its lower end. Calculate the period of torsional oscillations of the cylinder.

The torsional stiffness (the torque required to twist it through a unit angle) of the wire is given by:

$$k = \frac{\text{torque}}{\text{angle}} = \frac{JG}{L} = \frac{\pi d^4}{32} \times \frac{82 \times 10^9}{1} = 2.56 \times 10^{-3} \text{ N m rad}^{-1}$$

G is the shear modulus of the steel, see Chapter 9, and J is the polar second moment of area of the wire, see Chapter 11. The moment of inertia of a solid cylinder is (see below):

$$I = \frac{MD^2}{8} = \rho l \frac{\pi D^2}{4} \frac{D^2}{8} = 2.66 \times 10^{-3} \text{ kg m}^2$$

The equation of motion is (by analogy with a linear spring-mass system):

$$I\ddot{\theta} + k\theta = 0$$

so that the natural (circular) frequency is:

$$\omega_n = \left[\frac{k}{I}\right]^{\frac{1}{2}} = 0.98 \text{ rad s}^{-1}$$

The natural frequency is $\omega_n/2\pi = 0.156$ Hz, and the period is $2\pi/\omega_n = 6.4$ s. Notice that the same symbol and units are used for both angular velocity and circular frequency. In fact, the circular frequency is the maximum value of angular velocity reached during the motion. But to avoid confusion, it is usually best to treat them as separate quantities, and use different symbols or subscripts.

Example

An electric motor develops a constant torque (independent of speed) of 2.5 N m. It is directly coupled to a cast iron flywheel 22 cm in diameter and 5 cm thick. The total moment of inertia of the armature/flywheel assembly is 0.1 kg m². The system starts from rest. Calculate its rotational speed after 10 s.

The dimensions and material of the flywheel are not needed, though they would provide a check on the consistency of the data - they should produce a moment of inertia somewhat below the value given.

We ignore friction, air resistance (often called "windage" in electric motors), etc. The effect of these will be to reduce the available torque, probably in a way that rises with rotational speed.

The equation of motion is:

$$T = I\ddot{\theta}$$

so that $\ddot{\theta} = T/I = 25$ rad s^{-2} = const.

The kinematic constant acceleration equation is:

$$\dot{\theta} = \dot{\theta}_0 + \ddot{\theta}t \qquad \text{with} \qquad \dot{\theta}_0 = 0$$

whence when $t = 10$, $\dot{\theta} = 250$ rad s^{-1}, and rotational speed $= 250\times60/2\pi = 2387$ rev min^{-1}.

8.4 MOMENT OF INERTIA

The moment of inertia of a solid body is a function of the geometry and mass (or density) distribution of the body, and the direction and location of the axis concerned. A better name for it might be "second moment of mass".

For an elementary "mass on the end of a stick" body, $I = Mr^2$. For a body consisting of multiple masses, this becomes $I = \sum_i M_i r_i^2$. For a body with distributed mass, the values M_i become infinitesimals dm, and the summation becomes an integral over the whole mass, thus giving the equation given in section 8.3, above.

An alternative way of expressing moment of inertia is to write $I = Mk^2$, where M is the total mass of the body, and k is the *radius of gyration*, which can be thought of as a typical or average radius for an element of mass.

To distinguish the axis of rotation concerned, we use subscripts on I and k: I_O and k_O refer to an axis O. In three dimensional problems where the direction of the axis as well as its location are needed, the subscript is often doubled: I_{xx} and k_{xx}, etc.

Generally, the moment of inertia is calculated by direct integration. For example, for a solid uniform bar of radius R, length L and density ρ, rotating about its axis:

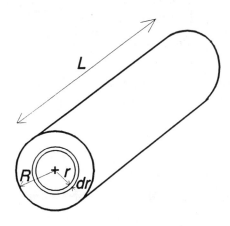

We divide the bar into elementary concentric tubes of radius r and thickness dr (Figure 8.5). The mass of one of these tubes is $dm = 2\pi\rho r L dr$, so that the moment of inertia is:

$$I = \int_0^R 2\pi\rho r L r^2 dr$$

$$= 2\pi\rho L \int_0^R r^3 dr$$

$$= \tfrac{1}{2}\pi\rho L R^4$$

Figure 8.5

Since the mass of the whole bar is $M = \pi\rho L R^2$, the radius of gyration is given by $k^2 = \tfrac{1}{2}R^2$. Notice that by working in terms of radius of gyration, we avoid having to bring in the overall length or the mass at this stage.

We can calculate the moment of inertia of a hollow cylinder (tube) just by changing the integration limits: $I = \tfrac{1}{2}\pi\rho L(R_2^4 - R_1^4) = \tfrac{1}{2}M(R_2^2 + R_1^2)$, where R_2 and R_1 are the outside and inside radii, respectively, or $k = \tfrac{1}{2}(R_2^2 + R_1^2)$.

Remember that if the density is not constant (e.g. for a rotor consisting of a steel shaft with an aluminium pulley on it), the integration will have to be split into parts allowing for the different densities.

The definition of moment of inertia is linear in the mass M. This means that if a rotor has two or more parts connected together, rotating about the same axis, the total moment of inertia is given by the sum of the moments of inertia of the different parts.

The expressions given for uniform solid and hollow circular section shafts will cover virtually all simple problems concerned with rotating machinery. Only in the case of non-uniform or unsymmetrical rotors (e.g. alternator rotors or systems with cams or cranks) will other methods be needed.

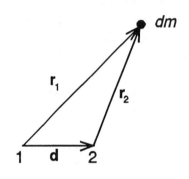

It is possible to calculate the moment of inertia about one axis, and then modify it to give that about another axis which is parallel to the first. Let the moments of inertia about the two axes be I_1 and I_2 respectively, and the vector between the axes be **d**. An element of mass dm has a position vector $\mathbf{r}_1$ relative to axis 1 and $\mathbf{r}_2$ relative to axis 2 (Figure 8.6). Then:

$$I_1 = \int_M r_1^2\, dm \qquad \text{and} \qquad I_2 = \int_M r_2^2\, dm$$

Figure 8.6

But (using vector notation):

$$r_1^2 = \mathbf{r}_1.\mathbf{r}_1 = (\mathbf{d} + \mathbf{r}_2).(\mathbf{d} + \mathbf{r}_2) = d^2 + r_2^2 + 2\mathbf{d}.\mathbf{r}_2$$

Integrating over the whole mass gives:

$$I_1 = \int_M r_1^2\, dm = \int_M d^2\, dm + \int_M r_2^2\, dm + \mathbf{d}.\int_M \mathbf{r}_2\, dm = Md^2 + I_2 + \mathbf{d}.\int_M \mathbf{r}_2\, dm$$

(since **d** is the same for all dm). If we choose axis 2 to be through the centre of mass G, then the last integral (the first moment of mass about G) is zero, by definition. We thus obtain the *Parallel Axes Theorem*:

$$I_X = I_G + Md^2 \qquad \text{or} \qquad k_X^2 = k_G^2 + d^2$$

which gives the moment of inertia or radius of gyration about an axis through a point X in terms of that about a parallel axis through the centre of mass G and the distance between the axes.

It follows from this that the moment of inertia about an axis through the centre of mass is smaller than that about any parallel axis.

Example

A steel coupling flange is a disk 20 cm *diameter and* 1 cm *thick, in which are drilled six equally spaced axial holes* 15 mm *diameter at a radius of* 8 cm *(Figure 8.7). Calculate its moment of inertia about its axis of symmetry.*

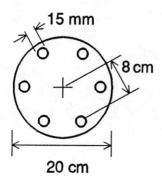

15 mm

8 cm

20 cm

Figure 8.7

The moment of inertia is equal to that of the blank flange (with no holes) minus that of the material which would fill the holes, all taken **about the axis** O through the centre of the flange:

$$I_{FO} = I_{BO} - 6 I_{HO}$$

where the first subscript refers to the **Flange**, Blank or Hole, and the second refers to the axis.

$$I_{BO} = \tfrac{1}{2}\rho \pi L R^4 \text{ (as above)} = 0.0123 \text{ kg m}^2.$$

Using the parallel axes theorem, $I_{HO} = I_{HG} + M_H R_H^2$ (where G is the centre of a hole). Whence:

$$I_{HG} = 3.90 \times 10^{-7} \text{ kg m}^2.$$

(using the same expression as for the blank flange)

$$M_H \text{ (the "mass of a hole")} = 0.0139 \text{ kg}$$

$$I_{HO} = 8.92 \times 10^{-5} \text{ kg m}^2.$$

And finally:

$$I_{FO} = 0.0123 - 6 \times 8.92 \times 10^{-5} = 0.0118 \text{ kg m}^2.$$

The mass of the flange is 2.466 - 6×0.0139 = 2.383 kg, and the radius of gyration = $\sqrt{(I/M)}$ = 0.070 m = 7 cm.

Definitions and formulae relating to Moment of Inertia are summarized in Appendix I.

8.5 GEARING

Gears are used to transfer torque from one rotating shaft to another. In the simplest cases the two shafts are parallel, but this is in no way essential; nor need they be in the same plane. Other ways of connecting shafts exist: belt or chain drives, electric or hydraulic torque converters, etc. The behaviour of these can be studied in a very similar manner to the approach we will use for gears.

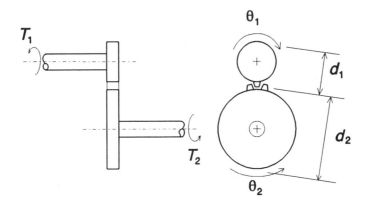

Figure 8.8

Figure 8.8 shows a simple pair of gears (only a few teeth are shown, highly diagrammatically). The gear diameters d_1 and d_2 are what are called *pitch circle diameters* - that is, the effective diameters of the gears, somewhere between the root diameter between teeth and the outside diameter across the teeth. The ratio d_2/d_1 is called the *gear ratio*. There is no standard as to which way up this ratio should be: either the input or output shaft or the larger or smaller diameter may be on top, with the other underneath. There is, perhaps, a slight preference for a ratio greater than 1 - i.e. with the larger diameter on top. The ratio is then said to be *step up* if the larger gear is on the input shaft, and *step down* if it is on the output.

The gear ratio determines the relative angles and speeds of rotation of the shafts. If the input shaft (shaft 1, for example) rotates through a small angle $d\theta_1$, any tooth on it will move a distance $dx = d\theta_1 \times d_1/2$ circumferentially. Where the gears mesh, a tooth of the output gear 2 must move the same distance, so that the angle that shaft 2 rotates through is given by

$$d\theta_2 = 2dx/d_2 = d\theta_1 \times d_1/d_2$$

The angles of rotation are thus in the inverse ratio of the gear diameters. The ratio of angular velocities will also be the inverse of the gear ratio. This is the reason for the terms *step up* and *step down*: they refer to the relative rotational speeds.

8.5.1 Steady rotation

Torque is transmitted from one shaft to the other by means of a pair of forces acting between the two meshing teeth. If the system is in steady rotation, the torque applied to either shaft must be equal and opposite to the moment of the inter-tooth force about the appropriate shaft centre. If this force is F:

$$T_1 = F\frac{d_1}{2} \qquad \text{and} \qquad T_2 = F\frac{d_2}{2}$$

$$\text{so that} \qquad \frac{T_1}{T_2} = \frac{d_1}{d_2}$$

The shaft torques are thus in the ratio of diameters. Here, we have tacitly assumed that there are no other forces with moments about the axes of the shafts. Generally, though, this is not the case. There will be friction between the two contacting surfaces which, since they will not always be radial, will have a moment about the axes. This leads to a reduction in torque in the output shaft compared to that calculated above. In a well designed and maintained gear system, however, the difference can be very small - of the order of 2%.

Note regarding signs: in this particular case, the two meshing gears rotate in opposite directions, and the torques in the two shafts are also in opposite directions. It is quite easy, however, to devise geometries in which both torques and rotations are in the same sense; this is normally the case for belt and chain drives. Furthermore, some gear systems (e.g. bevel gears) have non-parallel shafts, and the relative rotation directions may be difficult to describe. In defining torque transmission systems, it is generally necessary to specify the input and output shaft rotation directions as well as the gear ratio.

Power

Since the rotational speed is inversely proportional to the gear ratio, and the torque is directly proportional to it, the power transmitted (torque × angular velocity) is constant (neglecting losses, as discussed above). The gear system is directly analogous to an electrical transformer, where the voltage and current vary in inverse proportion, but their product, the power, remains constant.

Reaction

If the torques in the input and output shafts are different in sign, direction or magnitude, a free body diagram of the gear system as a whole will show an out of balance torque. In order to constrain this, extra moments are needed. These are provided by lateral forces in the bearings locating the shafts, and ultimately by the fixing down bolts of the gearbox. It is not possible to have an unconstrained gearbox (except for the trivial case of collinear input and output shafts rotating in the same sense at the same speed); a reaction torque must always be provided from somewhere.

8.5.2 Unsteady behaviour

If we know the moments of inertia of the two gears (and associated shafts), we can readily investigate the behaviour in acceleration. Consider the behaviour of the system when the load torque T_2 is zero:

$$I_1 \ddot{\theta}_1 = T_1 - F\frac{d_1}{2} \qquad\qquad I_2 \ddot{\theta}_2 = F\frac{d_2}{2}$$

$$\frac{\theta_1}{\theta_2} = \frac{d_2}{d_1} \qquad \therefore \quad \frac{\ddot{\theta}_1}{\ddot{\theta}_2} = \frac{d_2}{d_1}$$

$$\text{whence} \quad T_1 = (I_1 + I_2(\frac{d_1}{d_2})^2)$$

where F is the inter-tooth force, as above. Considering the system as a "black box", viewed from the input shaft, it behaves as if it was a single rotor of equivalent moment of inertia I':

$$I' = I_1 + I_2(\frac{d_1}{d_2})^2$$

Similarly, viewed from the output shaft, it would be:

$$I'' = I_2 + I_1(\frac{d_2}{d_1})^2$$

The idea of an equivalent moment of inertia may also be usefully applied to energy and momentum calculations. For example, the total kinetic energy of the system is:

$$\text{kinetic energy} = \tfrac{1}{2}I_1\dot{\theta}_1^2 + \tfrac{1}{2}I_2\dot{\theta}_2^2$$

$$= \tfrac{1}{2}(I_1 + I_2(\frac{d_1}{d_2})^2)\dot{\theta}_1^2$$

$$= \tfrac{1}{2}I'\dot{\theta}_1^2$$

$$= \tfrac{1}{2}I''\dot{\theta}_2^2$$

Example

A propulsion motor is geared to a ship's propeller through a stepdown gearbox of ratio 15:1. It delivers 10 000 kW at 3000 rev min⁻¹. The moment of inertia of the motor is 1000 kg m² and that of the propeller and shaft is 100 000 kg m². A wave lifts the propeller clear of the water for 3 s. Estimate the increase in motor speed (a) assuming constant motor power over this period, (b) assuming constant motor torque.

(a) All the power must have gone to increase the kinetic energy.
    Increase in energy = power × time = $10^7 \times 3 = 3 \times 10^7$ J
    Initial energy $= \tfrac{1}{2}I_1\omega_1^2 + \tfrac{1}{2}I_2\omega_2^2$
                   $= \tfrac{1}{2}(I_1 + I_2/n^2)\omega_1^2 = 7.128 \times 10^7$ J
    (where n is the gear ratio).
    Final energy $= 3 \times 10^7 + 7.128 \times 10^7 = 10.128 \times 10^7$ J
    Whence final speed $= 374.5$ rad s⁻¹ $= 3576$ rev min⁻¹,
    and the increase in motor speed is 576 rev min⁻¹.
        (This could also be done using acceleration equations, as below).

(b) Using the equivalent moment of inertia method, as above,

$$T = (I_1 + I_2/n^2)\ddot{\theta}$$

where $\ddot{\theta}$ is the motor speed. Integrating with respect to t with T constant gives the speed as a function of time:

$$\dot{\theta} = T/(I_1 + I_2/n^2)t + \text{const}$$

The constant of integration is the initial speed. (This equation could also be obtained by considerations of angular momentum and impulse.) Whence the increase in speed is 66.04 rad s⁻¹ $= 631$ rev min⁻¹.

8.6 SIMULTANEOUS ROTATION AND LINEAR MOTION

It is possible for a body to move in both rotation and linear motion simultaneously: for example a rolling ball. It can be shown quite generally that the two motions can be considered separately, provided that linear motion of the centre of mass and rotational motion about the centre of mass are considered.

Example

Calculate the velocity of a spherical ball after rolling down a 30° slope 1 m long.

Method 1: Let the final velocity be v and the corresponding rotational velocity be ω. So long as the ball is not slipping, these are related by $v = r\omega$. The final kinetic energy of the linear motion is $\frac{1}{2}mv^2$, and that of the rotational motion $\frac{1}{2}I_G\omega^2$. For a sphere, $I_G = 2mr^2/5$. Whence the final total kinetic energy is $7mv^2/10$. This must be equal to the initial potential energy, $mgh = mgl\sin30$. Therefore $v^2 = (10/7)gl\sin30$ and $v = 2.65$ m s^{-1}.

Method 2: Referring to Figure 8.9, there are two forces acting on the sphere in the direction of the plane: a component of its weight, $mg\sin30$ acting at the centre of mass, down the plane and the frictional force F at the point of contact, up the plane. Considering the linear motion of the centre of mass:

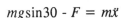

$$mg\sin30 - F = m\ddot{x}$$

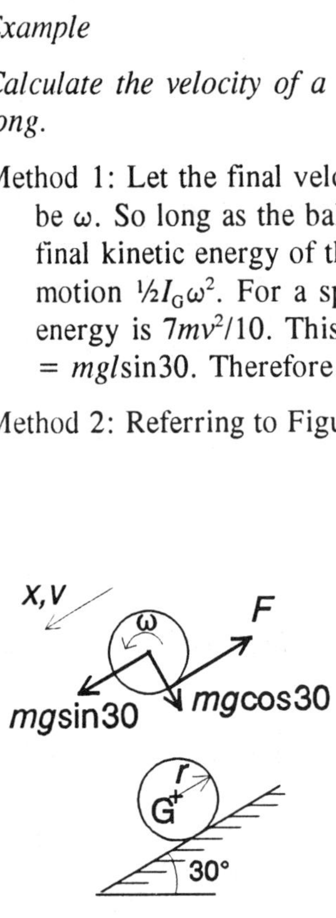

Only the frictional force has a moment about the centre of mass, and the rotational equation of motion is:

$$Fr = I_G\dot{\omega}$$

Figure 8.9

Eliminating the friction force F between these two equations, and using $v = \dot{x} = r\omega$ and the expression for the moment of inertia, as before, we obtain:

$$\ddot{x} = \frac{5}{7}g\sin30$$

This is a constant acceleration equation which can be integrated in the usual way, and gives the same result as above.

EXAMPLES

It is suggested that Appendix I is studied before these problems are attempted.

8.1   Calculate the moments of inertia of the following bodies about their axis of symmetry:
        (a) a steel flywheel 50 cm diameter and 5 cm thick;
        (b) a conical brass shaft 70 mm long, 10 mm diameter at the small end and 20 mm diameter at the large end;
        (c) a spoked wheel consisting of a hub (whose effect is ignored), 12 wooden spokes which may be assumed to be cylinders 0.5 m long and 50 mm diameter, and a wooden ring 1 m inside diameter, 1.1 m outside diameter and 8 cm wide, on which is a steel tyre 5 mm thick (assume wood has a density of 550 kg m^{-3});
        (d) a motor armature which is approximately an ellipsoid of revolution, with its long axis along the axis of rotation, 30 cm long and 15 cm maximum diameter, with an average relative density of 8.
        (e) an aluminium flange 150 mm diameter and 10 mm thick, with a boss 50 mm diameter and 40 mm long, and a shaft hole 25 mm diameter.
        (Ans: 2.41, 2.44$\times 10^{-6}$, 23.5, 0.064, 1.41$\times 10^{-3}$ kg m^2)

8.2   A robot arm (which may be considered to be a uniform aluminium alloy rod of diameter 50 mm and length 1 m) is pivoted about one end and carries a concentrated load of 5 kg at the other. The rod is swinging in a horizontal plane with an angular velocity of 2 rad s^{-1}. What constant torque must be applied at the pivot in order to bring it to rest within 3° of rotation?
        (Ans: 259 N m)

8.3   Flexible wire is stored on a wooden drum consisting of two flanges 250 mm diameter and 6 mm thick on each end of a cylindrical core 70 mm diameter and 200 mm long. The drum stands on its flanges with the free end of the wire leading away horizontally from the lower side of the core. A tension of 10 N is applied to the end of the wire, maintained for 0.5 s, and released. Neglecting any effects arising out of the stiffness or mass of the wire, and assuming the flanges do not slip, calculate the final rolling speed of the drum.
        (Ans: 4.28 m s^{-1})

8.4   A friction brake exerts a normal force of 180 N on the rim of a cast iron flywheel 30 cm diameter and 4 cm thick. The coefficient of friction between the flywheel and the brake material is 0.2. The wheel is rotating freely at 3000 rev min^{-1} when the brake is applied. Find how long it takes for the speed to fall to 100 rev min^{-1}.
        (Ans: 68 s)

8.5   A bucket of mass M is fastened to one end of a light rope which is coiled about a windlass of moment of inertia I and radius r. Find the acceleration of the bucket after it is released from rest.
(Ans: $g/(1 + I/Mr^2)$)

8.6   Using an energy method, find the velocity of the bucket in the previous question after it has fallen a distance x.
(Ans: $x^2 = 2gx/(1 + I/Mr^2)$)

8.7   A rolling mill of moment of inertia 5000 kg m^2 is driven through a clutch by a motor of moment of inertia 300 kg m^2. Initially, the motor is running at 375 rev min^{-1}, the clutch is disengaged, and the mill is stationary. The clutch is engaged and initially slips, but eventually stops slipping, so that the motor and mill are rotating at the same speed. Ignoring any motor or frictional torque, calculate the final speed. Qualitatively, what would be the effect of motor torque on (a) the final speed, and (b) the time for which the clutch slips?
(Ans: 21.2 rev min^{-1} (a) higher, (b) longer)

8.8   An electric motor driving a spindle of total moment of inertia 15×10^{-3} kg m^2 is spinning freely at 1500 rev min^{-1}. At a given instant, the motor is short-circuited, which produces a retarding torque of $\omega/100$ N m, where ω is the instantaneous angular velocity. Find how long it takes for the motor speed to be halved, and how many revolutions of the spindle occur in this time.
(Ans: 1.04 s, 17.75 revs)

8.9   A marble is rolled up a slope of 30° to the horizontal, at an initial speed of 3 m s^{-1}. There is no slipping between the marble and the surface. How far up does it get before stopping and rolling back?
(Ans: 1.28 m)

8.10   A spacecraft, which can be considered to be a uniform solid cylinder of radius 1 m and mass 1 tonne, is rotating about its axis of symmetry once every 10 s. A number of small nitrogen jets tangential to the outer surface are used to stop the rotation. The velocity of the jets is 200 m s^{-1}. What mass of nitrogen must be used?
(Ans: 1.57 kg)

BIBLIOGRAPHY

Higginson GR, *Foundations of Engineering Mechanics*. Longman, 1974 (Chapter 7)

Prentis J, *Engineering Mechanics*. Oxford, 1979 (Chapters 8 and 10)

Synge JL and Griffith BA, *Principles of Mechanics*. McGraw-Hill 1959 (Chapter 7)

Part 2
Basic Stress/Strain

9

Introduction

In Part 1 (Chapter 3), we considered how to calculate the support forces and tension or compression forces in members of statically determinate structures. In Part 2, we are concerned with the deformation of members when loaded. We will look first (Chapter 9) at how loads are carried within materials, and how structures change their size and shape as a result of the loads. In Chapter 10, we consider transverse loads which produce bending. Chapter 11 is concerned with rotational loading: twisting or torsion. In Chapter 12, we will compare real materials with the idealized models used previously. Finally in Chapter 13 we will consider some of the ways in which structures may fail.

9.1 STRESS AND STRAIN

All structures deflect when load is applied to them, and usually the deflection increases as the load increases. The amount of deflection is very dependent on the geometries and materials of the various members.

If we consider a uniform bar of initial length L and cross-sectional area A (Figure 9.1) to which we apply a load F, we can measure a change in length δL. An identical bar of twice the length would change in length by twice as much (consider it as two short bars end to end, each increasing by δL). Thus the ratio $\delta L/L$ is a constant for a given force, and is independent of the length. This ratio

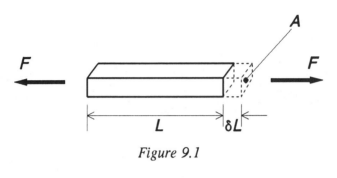

Figure 9.1

$$\epsilon = \frac{\text{change in length}}{\text{original length}}$$

is called the *strain*. Being a ratio of two lengths, it is dimensionless and has no units. For some materials it can be quite large: a rubber band can easily double in length ($\epsilon = 1$). But for stiffer materials, it is often very small indeed: a typical value for steel might be 5×10^{-4}, or 0.05%. To cope with such small values, we often use microstrain, $\mu\epsilon$; the above value would be 500 $\mu\epsilon$.

Using a similar argument, we could lie two identical bars side by side, and apply twice the force to the pair to get the same deflection (or strain) in each. So the strain really depends not on force, but on force per unit area, or *stress*, σ, whose units are N m^{-2}. Here again, the basic unit is not always convenient, and for many applications we will be talking in terms of MN m^{-2}, sometimes also (confusingly) written as N mm^{-2}. The convention is that tensile stresses (those tending to pull the material apart) are considered to be positive. The pascal Pa (or MPa) is also occasionally used for stress. This is incorrect - it is the unit of pressure, which is negative stress, and is usually used in fluid mechanics. It is, however, the same size as the N m^{-2}.

There is an implicit assumption here that the load is carried uniformly across the area of the member, so that the stress is the same at any point on the cross-section. For members in pure tension or compression, this is often quite a reasonable assumption. For more complicated cases such as bending, though, this is not the case, as we shall see in Chapter 10.

By considering strain to depend on stress (rather than extension being a function of force), we can almost completely eliminate the geometry of the structure and identify underlying properties of the material itself.

These definitions of strain and stress are rather different (and much more precise) than the common usage where strain, stress, load, pressure and various other terms are used more or less interchangeably, and often figuratively. In engineering, each of them has its own precise meaning, and it is important to use them correctly.

9.2 ELASTIC MATERIALS

For most solid materials, there is a wide range of stress over which strain is a function of stress only. Moreover, it turns out that the relationship between stress and strain is often linear to a good approximation. Such materials are described as *linear elastic* (or just *elastic*). Then:

$$\sigma = E\epsilon$$

where E is called the *elastic modulus* (or Young's modulus). Since strain is dimensionless, E has the same units as stress. Since strain is (usually) very small, E is (usually) numerically much larger than σ.

A typical value of E for steel is 207×10^9 N m^{-2} (207 GN m^{-2}). A typical stress might be 150 MN m^{-2}, leading to a strain of 750 $\mu\epsilon$ (0.075%). We will look at the properties of various types of real materials in more detail in Chapter 12, including consideration of how accurately they are linear and elastic. A number of numerical values are tabulated in Appendix IV.

9.2.1 Directions

We have applied all our stresses in one direction. Clearly, we could apply stresses separately in all three co-ordinate directions. The three stresses σ_x, σ_y and σ_z then produce corresponding strains ϵ_x, ϵ_y and ϵ_z respectively. In the general case, the elastic modulus E may be different in different directions. Such materials are *anisotropic* (e.g. glassfibre composites, wood, reinforced concrete). But many common materials, including most metals, are isotropic, and have the same elastic modulus for all directions.

There is one further complication - a stress in one direction, say σ_x, produces strains in the y and z directions as well. A rubber band gets noticeably thinner as it is stretched, and the same applies to other materials. For a linear isotropic material, the strain is a fraction of that in the x direction:

$$\epsilon_y = -\nu\epsilon_x = -\nu\sigma_x/E \text{ (and similarly for the other pairs)}$$

The negative sign is because a positive stress in one direction produces a negative strain in the perpendicular directions. ν is called *Poisson's Ratio*, and is a material property. Its value is about 0.3 for most metals, 0.5 for rubbers and polymers and 0 for cork (which stops corks getting thinner and falling out as soon as you stop pushing them in).

When we have simultaneous stresses in two directions, the strains they produce are additive. For example, with stresses σ_x and σ_y, the strain in the x direction will be $\epsilon_x = \sigma_x/E - \nu\sigma_y/E$.

Since each of the three stresses causes strains in all three directions, a full analysis of *tri-axial* stress and strain can become very complex. In most of the applications we will look at, however, it is unnecessary.

9.2.2 Change of volume

A particular tri-axial stress system which is not too complicated is the *hydrostatic* system, where all the three components σ_x, σ_y and σ_z are equal. This is the same as that produced by a uniform fluid pressure p. The sign convention is that compressive pressure and tensile stress are positive, so that $\sigma_x = \sigma_y = \sigma_z = \sigma = -p$. In this case, all three strains will be equal:

$$\epsilon_x = \epsilon_y = \epsilon_z = \epsilon = \sigma(1 - 2v)/E$$

The change δV in volume V of a linear isotropic material under hydrostatic stress is given by:

$$\frac{(V + \delta V)}{V} = \frac{(x + \delta x)^3}{x^3} = (1 + \frac{\delta x}{x})^3 = (1 + \epsilon)^3 \simeq 1 + 3\epsilon$$

$$\therefore \frac{\delta V}{V} \simeq 3\epsilon$$

(where x and δx are a typical linear dimension and the change in it) so long as $\epsilon << 1$. We can define the *bulk modulus of elasticity*, K by:

$$K = \frac{\sigma}{\delta V/V} = \frac{E}{3(1 - 2v)}$$

The three material properties E, K and v are thus not independent. Knowledge of any two allows the third to be obtained. Since v is roughly 1/3 for common materials, K is roughly equal to E. For liquids and gases, E has no meaning - we cannot stress them in one direction only - but K can still be defined in the same way. The above equation shows that there will be no change in volume (the bulk modulus will be infinite) for materials with $v = 0.5$. Values of v larger than 0.5 would intuitively seem to be impossible. This is by and large the case, though it should be remembered that this formula applies only to linear isotropic materials undergoing small strains.

9.3 SHEAR

Some structures carry loads which are tangential to the surfaces to which they are applied. For example, a bicycle brake acts tangentially to the rim. Such forces are called *shear forces*, and the associated forces per unit area are *shear stresses* (when a distinction is needed, stresses perpendicular to the area on which they act are called *direct* or *normal stresses*).

Shear stresses have two directions associated with them - the direction of the force and the direction of the surface on which it acts (specified by its normal).

For example, the stress τ_{xy} is a stress in the y direction on the yz plane (i.e. the plane normal to the x direction), while τ_{zy} is also a stress in the y direction, but acting on the xy plane. Six distinct components of shear stress can be identified - see Figure 9.2. There will also be shear stresses on the 3 hidden planes of Figure 9.2. These may be found in any particular case by considering equilibrium in the $x,y,$ and z directions.

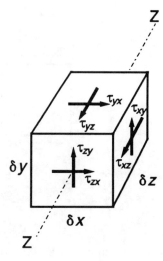

Figure 9.2

The six components of shear stress are not all independent. Referring again to Figure 9.2, we may look at the moment of the forces produced by the shear stresses about the axis ZZ parallel to the z direction through the centre of the cuboid. The forces produced by τ_{xy} and τ_{yx} have moments about this axis, but none of the others do since either they are parallel to it (τ_{xz} and τ_{yz}) or their effective line of action intercepts it (τ_{zy} and τ_{zx}). The moment produced by τ_{xy} is

$$\tau_{xy} \; (\delta z \; \text{x} \; \delta y) \; \text{x} \; \tfrac{1}{2} \; \delta x$$

and that produced by τ_{yx} is

$$\tau_{yx} \; (\delta z \; \text{x} \; \delta x) \; \text{x} \; \tfrac{1}{2} \; \delta y$$

These moments must balance (for equilibrium in rotation), and it follows that $\tau_{xy} = \tau_{yx}$ in all situations. A similar argument applies to the other two pairs of shear stresses.

These are termed *complementary shear stresses*. A shear stress on one plane is always accompanied by an equal shear stress on a perpendicular plane; there are thus only three independent components of shear stress.

While a direct stress produces a linear deflection (Figure 9.1), a shear stress produces an angular or *shear strain*, γ (Figure 9.3). (This is somewhat simplified - there should also be complementary shear stresses and associated shear strains.) For a linear material, the shear strain is proportional to the shear stress:

$$\gamma = \tau / G$$

where G is the *shear modulus* or *modulus of rigidity*. Since shear strain is non-dimensional, the shear modulus has the same dimensions and units as Young's modulus. It is a material property, and it can be shown that it is related to the other elastic moduli:

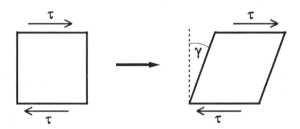

Figure 9.3

$$G = \tfrac{1}{2} E/(1 + \nu)$$

A typical value of ν is 0.3, so that G is about 38% of E.

9.4 CALCULATION OF STRESSES, STRAINS AND EXTENSIONS

The average direct stress in a load bearing component is calculated by dividing the load by the cross-sectional area. For example, a mass of 100 kg is suspended on a rod 5 mm diameter. The load is $100g = 981$ N, and the cross-sectional area is $\pi(0.005)^2/4 = 1.96 \times 10^{-5}$ m². The average stress is therefore $981/1.96 \times 10^{-5} = 5 \times 10^5$ N m⁻² (0.5 MN m⁻²). The stress is positive, since it is tensile.

The value calculated in this way is the average stress over the cross-section. However, we generally have no way of being sure that the stress is uniform. It might, for example, be higher near the centre of the component than near the edge. The maximum stress is always above the average, so this could lead us to overestimate the load carrying capacity of our system. The actual detail of how the stress is distributed depends on many factors, among which are the detailed geometry of the component and the fittings at the ends of it which transfer the load into or out of it, and its previous history which might have involved pre-stressing or heat treatment. Such matters are very much for specialists. We may note, however, that if stress is not uniform, some part of a component may not be carrying as much load as it could. From this point of view, an efficient structure is one where the stress is as uniformly distributed as possible, and all parts take their fair share of the load. We will come back to this topic in Chapter 13, when we consider stress concentrations and safety factors.

In Chapter 3, we considered various types of joints, and how it is often possible to idealize them to simple pin joints, since the influences of the details of the joints only extend over a comparatively short distance (St Venant's Principle). The same applies in this context. Once we are away from the immediate influence of end fittings, point loads, etc. it is often reasonable to assume that stresses are uniformly distributed. We will make this assumption, unless stated otherwise.

9.4.1 Ties, struts and columns

Under the assumption of uniform stress distribution, the calculation of the tensile stress in a tie or the compressive stress in a strut or column is straightforward. The only factor to take into account is whether the weight of the member has to be considered.

Examples

1. Calculate the stress, strain and extension of a steel cable 10 m *long, of cross-sectional area* 25 mm², *supporting a mass of* 1 tonne.

The weight of the 1 tonne mass is $1000g$ N. The weight of the cable is approximately $2g$ N, and is negligible in comparison to the load. The average stress in the cable is $\sigma = F/A = 1000g/25 \times 10^{-6} = 3.92 \times 10^8$ N m^{-2} (392 MN m^{-2}). For steel $E = 207$ GN m^{-2}, so that the strain will be $\sigma/E = 3.92 \times 10^8/207 \times 10^9 = 1.90 \times 10^{-3}$ (0.19 %). The extension is the strain times the length, 19 mm. The stress of 392 MN m^{-2} calculated here is, as we shall see later, uncomfortably high for any but the highest strength steels.

2. Calculate the compressive stress in a brick wall.

If we ignore any roof or other load supported by the wall, the stress arises from the weight of the bricks alone. At any given height, the load is the total weight of brick above that height. Consider a cross-sectional area A above which is a height h of brick. The load is ρgAh, where ρ is the density of brick, and is compressive. The stress is the load per unit area, ρgh (which is, of course, the same as the pressure at a depth h below the surface of a liquid). For (dry) brick, $\rho \simeq 200$ kg m^{-3}, so the stress is about $2000h$ N m^{-2}, where h is the distance from the top of the wall. The compressive strength of common brick is around 30 MN m^{-2}, so that a wall could be about $30 \times 10^6/2000 = 15$ km high before this was exceeded. This is one of the features that makes brick a very useful building material.

Buckling

All simple problems of ties, struts and columns can be solved in a similar manner. We must beware, however, that we are solving the right problem for struts. There is a critical load, usually very much lower than the compressive strength, beyond which a long, thin strut cannot be used because it will buckle, or bend sideways in an unstable manner. This load, known as the Euler buckling load, depends only on the strut geometry and its Young's modulus. If loaded above the buckling load, the strut will collapse sideways, unless prevented by non-linear effects. The buckling phenomenon can, however, be put to good use in applications such as springs in electrical switches, which are made to have two stable buckled configurations, and to snap between them when the switch is operated.

9.4.2 Shear stress

Shear stresses are calculated in a similar way to direct stresses, with similar reservations about whether they are uniformly distributed.

Example

A motor of weight 500 N is bolted to a vertical wall by four horizontal bolts 1 cm diameter, as shown in Figure 9.4. Calculate the shear stress in the bolts.

First assumption: the load is equally divided between the four bolts, so that each bolt carries 125 N. Second assumption: the stress is uniformly distributed across the bolts. The shear stress is thus given by:

$$\tau = 125/(\pi \times 0.01^2/4) = 1.59 \text{ MN m}^{-2}.$$

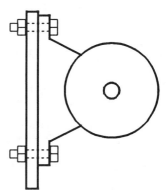

Figure 9.4

9.5 PRESSURE VESSELS

Struts and ties are one-dimensional systems. The load is applied in one direction only. In many applications, however, loads are applied in more than one direction, and the problem is two or three dimensional. Also, loads may be distributed over an area, rather than applied at a point. A common case is the pressure vessel: an enclosed structure is subjected to an internal pressure. Consider the cylindrical vessel in Figure 9.5. Although we have not drawn them, there must somewhere be ends on this vessel. The internal pressure exerts a force on the ends of $\pi R^2 p$, outwards on each end. This outwards force must be provided by tension in the cylindrical shell of the vessel. The cross-sectional area of the ends is $2\pi Rt$ (assuming that the thickness t is much less than the radius R). This means there must be a *longitudinal stress* σ_x in the material of the shell whose average value is given by:

$$\sigma_x = \pi R^2 p/2\pi Rt = pR/2t$$

There is also a stress in the circumferential direction. If we imagine the shell split across a diameter, the pressure will produce an outward force $2Rp$ per unit

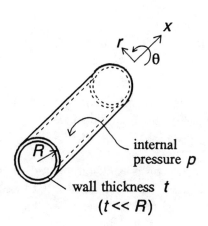

internal
pressure p

wall thickness t

$(t \ll R)$

Figure 9.5

length, which is balanced by the inward force due to the circumferential or *hoop stress* of $2t\sigma_\theta$ (Figure 9.6):

$$\sigma_\theta = pR/t$$

The hoop stress is twice the longitudinal stress. This is the reason that pipes subject to excess internal pressure (such as frozen water pipes or sausages being fried) split lengthwise rather than crosswise.

There is also a radial stress, σ_r. At the inner surface of the vessel, this must be a compressive stress of the same order of magnitude as p. It is not simple to calculate how it varies through the thickness of the material, but it is unlikely ever to be larger than p. But since both the longitudinal and hoop stresses are of order of magnitude pR/t, and $R \gg t$, the radial stress must be much less than either of the others, and is usually ignored.

The stresses calculated above are average values over the thickness of the material. In general, there will be

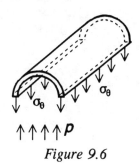

Figure 9.6

variation through the thickness, but this will be small in so far as the thickness is much less than the radius. A radius to thickness ratio of 10 is satisfactory in practise. The stresses in a pressure vessel whose walls are not thin compared to the radius are much harder to evaluate, and are not considered here.

By an exactly similar method, the hoop stress in a sphere is given by:

$$\sigma_\theta = pR/2t$$

and is the same in all directions, by symmetry. This is less than the longitudinal stress in a cylinder, so that (more expensive) spherical pressure vessels may be used in preference to cylindical ones in critical situations.

Example

Calculate the stresses in a plastic balloon which is approximately cylindrical in shape, 12 cm diameter and 40 cm long, made of material 0.1 mm thick, and with an internal pressure of 5 kPa.

The thickness is very small compared to the radius. The length does not really matter, except to validate the assumption of a cylindrical shape.

The longitudinal stress is $pR/2t = 5000 \times 0.12/1 \times 10^4 = 6$ MN m^{-2}. The hoop stress is twice this, 12 MN m^{-2}.

The stress in a cylindrical or spherical vessel is proportional to the radius of curvature. A flat surface has an infinite radius, so that if we made a flat-sided pressure vessel - a cube for example - it would be unable to carry any load at all. The internal pressure would distort the flat surface into a curve which, provided the matrial was adequately strong, would then be able to withstand it. In cases where flat sides are desirable (for example, in the firebox region of a steam locomotive boiler), internal stay bolts must be provided to support them. The ends of cylindrical pressure vessels such as gas cylinders and air compressor receivers are invariably made approximately spherical, protruding either outwards or inwards.

EXAMPLES

9.1   The ultimate tensile stress of nylon is 80 MN m^{-2}, and its density is 1150 kg m^{-3}. What is the maximum length of a nylon cord hanging vertically?
(Ans: 7091 m)

9.2   A cylindrical steel steam boiler 1 m diameter is to work at a pressure of 15 bar (gauge). The tensile strength of the steel is 500 MN m^{-2}, and the design is to have a safety factor of 10. What wall thickness should be used? What will be the increase in diameter of the boiler when at its working pressure? (Neglect thermal expansion of the boiler and change of material properties with temperature.)
(Ans: 15 mm, 0.24 mm)

9.3   A steel bolt 10 mm in diameter has a thread of pitch 1 mm. It is used to fasten together two components of total thickness 300 mm. Neglecting any change in size of the components, calculate the tension in the bolt if the nut is tightened 1/6 of a turn beyond the point where it just contacts the component surface. Would this be larger or smaller than the tension if change in size of the components was not neglected?
(Ans: 9.03 kN, larger)

9.4 Two bars joined by side plates and 10 mm diameter bolts are shown in Figure 9.7. Calculate the shear stress in the bolts for a tension of 20 kN in the bars.

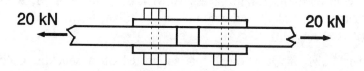

Figure 9.7

(Ans: 127 MN m^{-2})

9.5 A long steel tube 75 mm internal diameter and 1.5 mm wall thickness forms part of a heat exchanger. With its ends plugged, it is to be tested under internal pressure. The maximum allowable stress is 350 MN m^{-2}. In service, a safety factor of 3 will be used. Estimate (a) the test pressure which should be applied, (b) the working pressure which may be used, (c) the percentage increase in volume under test conditions, and (d) the increase in diameter under working pressure.
(Ans: 140 bar, 46.7 bar, 0.32%, 0.036 mm)

9.6 Figure 9.8 shows a pulley keyed to a 25 mm diameter shaft. The key is 6 mm square and 25 mm long. The maximum permitted shear stress in the key is 210 MN m^{-2}. Assuming a safety factor of 3, what is the maximum torque that can be transmitted?

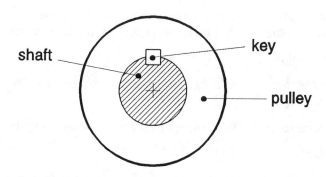

Figure 9.8

(Ans: 131 Nm)

9.7   A hoist is to lift the casing off a steam turbine for maintenance. The hoist has a six-fold purchase, and the mass of the casing is 300 kg. Nylon cord (maximum stress 70 MN m^{-2}) will be used, with a safety factor of 5. Calculate the minimum cord diameter (assuming solid cord). (Ans: 16.4 mm)

9.8   The hoist of Question 9.7 is supported on a shackle. Calculate the minimum diameter for the shackle pin if the maximum allowable shear stress is 100 MN m^{-2}, with a safety factor of 4. (Ans: 8.7 mm)

9.9   The total length of cord under load in the hoist of Question 9.7 is 25 m. Calculate the length of cord which must be wound in from when the hoist is just taut to when the casing just lifts off. Calculate also the strain energy stored in the cord. (Young's modulus for Nylon: 2.4 GN m^{-2}) (Ans: 146 mm, 215 J)

9.10   A boiler 0.5 m diameter has a working pressure of 7 bar. The top of the boiler is riveted onto the drum using 40 rivets each of diameter 12 mm. The base is bolted on with a flange, with 30 bolts of 16 mm diameter. Calculate the shear stress in the rivets and the tensile stress in the bolts, stating your assumptions in both cases. (Ans: 30.4 MN m^{-2}, 22.8 MN m^{-2})

BIBLIOGRAPHY

The following works cover the whole area of **Part 2: Basic Stress/Strain.** Separate bibliographies are not included in the remaining chapters.

General Introduction:

Gordon JE, *The New Science of Strong Materials, or Why You Don't Fall through the Floor*. Penguin, 1968

Gordon JE, *Structures, or Why Things Don't Fall Down*. Penguin, 1978

Fully Detailed:

Benham PP and Crawford RJ, *Mechanics of Engineering Materials*. Longman, 1987

Benham PP and Warnock FV, *Mechanics of Solids and Structures*. Pitman, 1973

Van Vlack LH, *Materials for Engineering*. Addison Wesley, 1982

10

Bending

In the last chapter, we considered deflections of components which were loaded along their length. Here, we will look at what happens when they are transversely loaded. We will confine ourselves to statically determinate cases, and will assume that deflections are small compared with other dimensions (which implies that angles and slopes are also small).

10.1 SHEAR FORCE AND BENDING MOMENT

When a beam carries a load at a position other than directly over a support, the load must be transmitted along the length of the beam. We can find the load at any point along the beam by looking at the free body diagram of part of it.

Figure 10.1a

Figure 10.1b

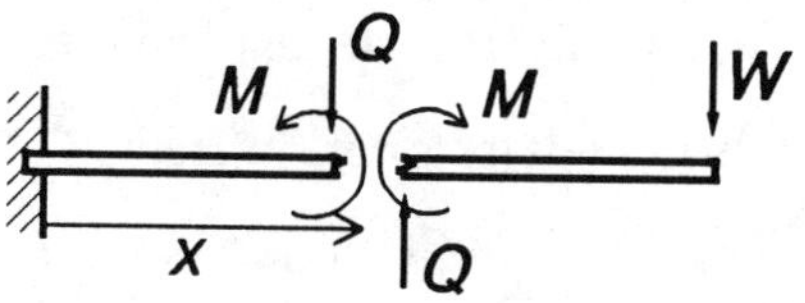

Consider a cantilever of length L carrying a load W (Figure 10.1a). If we (notionally) cut it at some position x, we will have to apply forces to the cut ends to maintain the two parts of the beam in equilibrium (Figure 10.1b). These forces will in general be a transverse force Q, the *shear force* and a moment M, the *bending moment*.

Q and M always appear in equal and opposite pairs, applied to the two ends. By considering the equilibrium of either half, we can find how they vary with x. In this case, the right-hand half is easier. Clearly, Q is constant, equal to W, while $M = -W(L - x)$, treating the directions of the arrows on the diagram as positive. At $x = 0$ (the fixed end), $M = -WL$ and at the other end ($x = L$) there is no bending moment. The same results could have been obtained from the left-hand half.

10.1.1 Shear force and bending moment diagrams

It is often useful to draw Shear Force and Bending Moment diagrams, which show how these quantities vary over the length of the beam. For the cantilever of Figure 10.1, they are as in Figure 10.2.

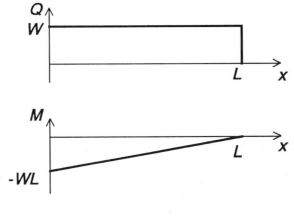

Figure 10.2

Sign Conventions

To avoid confusion, we need an unambiguous sign convention. Unfortunately, there is not a universal standard, but the following is widely used:

    1. x increases from left to right;

    2. y increases from top to bottom (i.e. positive downwards);

    3. Positive loads and deflections are downwards.

4. Shear force is positive if it tends to produce a clockwise rotation;

5. Bending moment is positive if it tends to make the beam sag (i.e. to be concave on its upper surface).

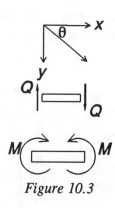

The last two are needed because shear force and bending moment always appear in equal and opposite pairs; if one particular direction was chosen as positive, we would also have to specify which side of the cut we are considering.

Figure 10.3

10.1.2 Simply supported beam with point load

Figure 10.4 shows a beam simply supported at its ends and carrying a point load in between. It is statically determinate, and the support reactions shown are readily obtained be vertical equilibrium and by taking moments about one end. The force balance for shear force and bending moment will depend on whether we cut the beam to the left of the load or to its right.

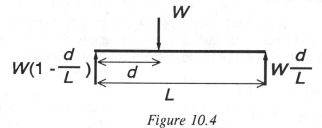

Figure 10.4

In the first case, considering the left-hand half, we get

$$Q = W(1 - \frac{d}{L}) \qquad M = W(1 - \frac{d}{L})x$$

while for the second case (for which it is easier to consider the right-hand half),

$$Q = -W\frac{d}{L} \qquad M = Wd(1 - \frac{x}{L})$$

The shear force and bending moment diagrams are as in Figure 10.5. In general, Q is constant between point loads, and changes by (minus) the amount of the load, at the load. Supports behave in a similar manner, as negative loads. *M* varies linearly between point loads, and changes slope at the load.

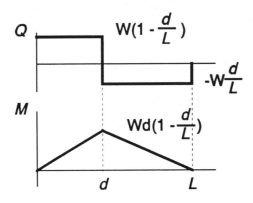

Figure 10.5

10.1.3 Distributed loads

Not all loads can be considered as point loads. For example, the weight of a beam is itself a load, and is distributed along the length. Similarly for a self-supporting pipeline, the load (the liquid in the pipe) is distributed.

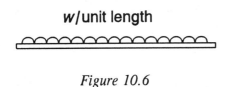

Figure 10.6

A useful idealisation is the *uniformly distributed load*, whose magnitude is described in terms of force per unit length (Figure 10.6).

When we cut the beam to obtain the shear force and bending moment, we have to calculate the amount of load on the cut section, and the effective position at which it acts. For example, for the cantilever carrying a uniformly distributed load in Figure 10.7, the load carried by the right-hand section is $w(L - x)$, and its centre of action is at the mid-point of the section. We find that the shear force

$$Q = w(L - x)$$

varies linearly with *x*, rather than being constant, and the bending moment

$$M = -w(L - x)\frac{L - x}{2}$$

varies quadratically. The shear force and bending moment diagrams are shown in Figure 10.8.

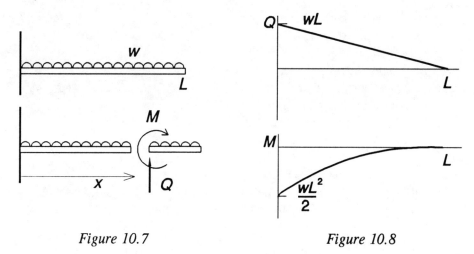

Figure 10.7   Figure 10.8

A similar analysis for a simply supported beam with a uniformly distributed load is shown in Figure 10.9. Note that, by symmetry, the support forces are equal and there can be no shear force at the centre of the beam.

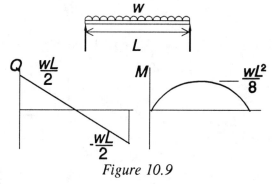

Figure 10.9

10.1.4 Combinations of loads

The process is the same for more complex cases: shear force changes abruptly at point loads, and linearly with uniformly distributed loads, while bending moment changes slope at point loads and varies parabolically for uniformly distributed loads. Figure 10.10 shows an example. Notice the *point of contraflexure*, where the bending moment is zero, and the beam is in pure shear. A hinge could be inserted at that point without affecting the ability of the beam to withstand this particular load combination. Inserting a hinge might not be a very useful thing to do, but this might be a good choice of position to join two components together.

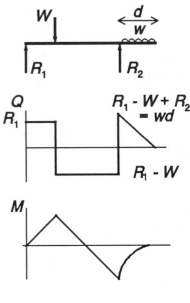

Figure 10.10

10.1.5 Non-uniformly distributed loads

Although the approach is the same, it will often be necessary to integrate, perhaps numerically or graphically, to find the shear force and bending moment in particular cases. The diagrams in general will not be straight lines or simple curves.

10.1.6 Relationship between shear force and bending moment

Since Q and M are calculated from the same data, they are obviously not independent of each other. Consider the small element of a beam shown in Figure 10.11. Over the length δx the bending moment increases from M to $M + \delta M$, the shear force increases from Q to $Q + \delta Q$, and there is an external load δF (assumed to act at $\delta x/2$). Taking moments about the left-hand end, we obtain:

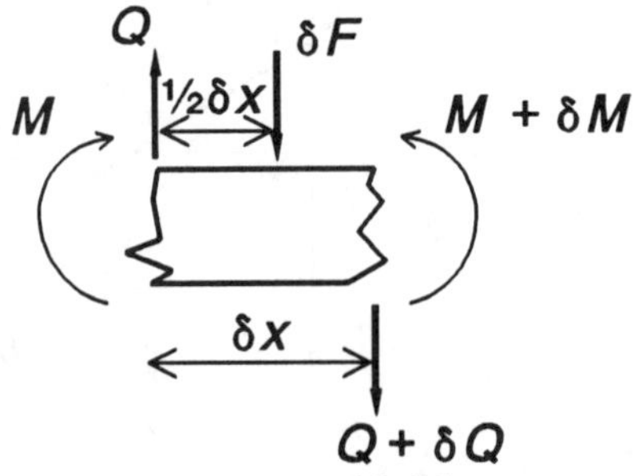

Figure 10.11

$$M - (M + \delta M) + (Q + \delta Q)\delta x + \delta F\frac{\delta x}{2} = 0$$

$$\therefore \quad -\delta M + Q\delta x + \delta Q\delta x + \delta F\frac{\delta x}{2} = 0$$

The last two terms are small compared to the first two. Neglecting these, and taking the limit:

$$Q = \frac{dM}{dx}$$

Q is thus the slope of the bending moment diagram. To obtain M from Q, we can integrate the shear force diagram, using an end condition to evaluate the constant of integration.

10.2 MACAULAY'S NOTATION

In the examples above, when calculating the shear force and bending moment, we had to state what point on the beam we were considering, and the resulting expressions changed when we passed a point load or support. This is inconvenient: it would be better if we had one expression which covered the whole beam. *Macaulay's Notation* provides such an expression. Consider again the simply supported beam with a point load, of Figure 10.4. The bending moments for the two sections, left and right of the load, are:

$$M = W(1 - \frac{d}{L})x \quad \text{and} \quad M = Wd(1 - \frac{x}{L})$$
$$(x < d) \qquad\qquad\qquad (x > d)$$

Using a special square bracket notation, these can be combined and written:

$$M = W(1 - \frac{d}{L})x - W[x - d]$$

where: $[x - d] = 0$ when $x < d$

and $[x - d] = (x - d)$ when $x > d$

The first term is due to the left-hand support. The second is due to the point load, and is zero if we are to the left of the load, non-zero to the right.

The method can readily be extended to multiple point loads or distributed loads covering only part of the beam. The bending moment is calculated for the farthest right section of the beam, and each separate term enclosed in "Macaulay brackets". Each of these terms is zero if its contents is negative, otherwise it takes the value of its contents.

In the event of a distributed load ending before the right hand end of the beam, we need some way of "stopping" the term at the end of the load. A simple way of doing this is to extend the load to the end, and add another negative load, as shown in Figure 10.12:

Figure 10.12

In calculating beam deflections (see section 10.6 below), we need to integrate the bending moment with respect to x. Macaulay brackets are integrated just like any other term; they are always linear in x inside the bracket, although the whole may be raised to some power. For example, a uniformly distributed load may produce a term like $\frac{w}{2}[x - a]^2$. This would integrate to $\frac{w}{6}[x - a]^3$. The integral is still a Macaulay bracket, and takes the appropriate value when numerical values are substituted.

10.3 SUPERPOSITION

Since both shear force and bending moment vary linearly with load (W, w, etc), we can use the principle of superposition. For example, the loading system in Figure 10.13 can be split into two parts and the bending moments (or shear forces) for the two cases calculated separately and then added together (graphical methods are often useful for this).

10.4 BENDING STRESSES AND STRAINS

The shear force and bending moment carried by a beam arise from stresses within the material of the beam. These stresses result in strains, which in their turn result in the beam deforming in some way. This deformation takes the form of a curvature of the beam, and a deflection from the original position - the beam bends.

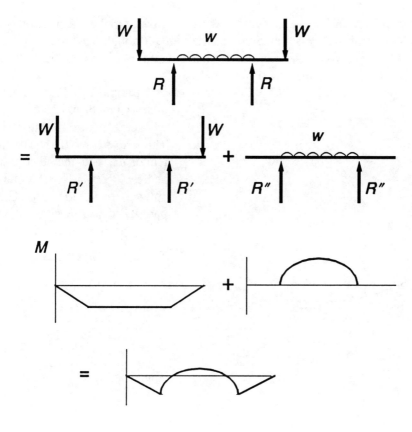

Figure 10.13

When a simply supported beam bends under a vertical load, the top surface gets shorter (negative strain) and the bottom surface gets longer (positive strain), as in Figure 10.14. This means that the top surface must be in compression (negative stress) and the bottom surface in tension (positive stress).

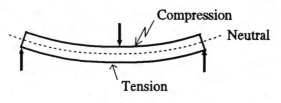

Figure 10.14

Somewhere in between, there must be a point (or rather, a surface) where there is no strain. This is called the *neutral plane* (though it is rarely a true flat plane). At any given cross-section, the horizontal line across the beam through the neutral plane is called the *neutral axis*.

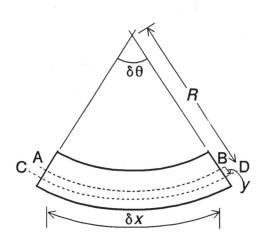

Figure 10.15

In Figure 10.15, we consider a short length of the bent beam whose radius of curvature is R. The arc AB of the beam is of length δx, and includes a small angle $\delta\theta$. AB is the neutral "plane", and the arc CD is parallel to it at position y below it (the positive direction).

The length of arc AB is

$$\delta x = R\delta\theta$$

while that of CD is

$$(R + y)\delta\theta$$

The strain in CD is given by

$$\epsilon_x = \frac{CD - AB}{AB}$$

$$= \frac{(R + y)\delta\theta - R\delta\theta}{R\delta\theta}$$

$$= \frac{y}{R}$$

Thus at any given point x along the beam, *the strain due to bending varies linearly* from a maximum tensile value at the bottom, through zero at the neutral plane to a maximum compressive value at the top. This result is independent of the material properties; it is a purely geometrical result. Note that we do not know (yet) exactly where the neutral plane is, and the maximum positive and negative strains are not necessarily the same. These factors depend on the shape of the beam cross section.

If the material is linear elastic, the *stresses* also vary linearly from top to bottom of the beam. We can now calculate the position of the neutral axis. Figure 10.16 shows a cross section of a beam, shown as rectangular for simplicity, but may be any shape.

Since there is no axial force in the beam, the total effect of the positive and negative stresses must be zero:

$$\int_A \sigma_x dA = 0$$

$$\therefore \quad \int_A \frac{yE}{R} dA = 0$$

it follows that $\int_A y dA = 0$

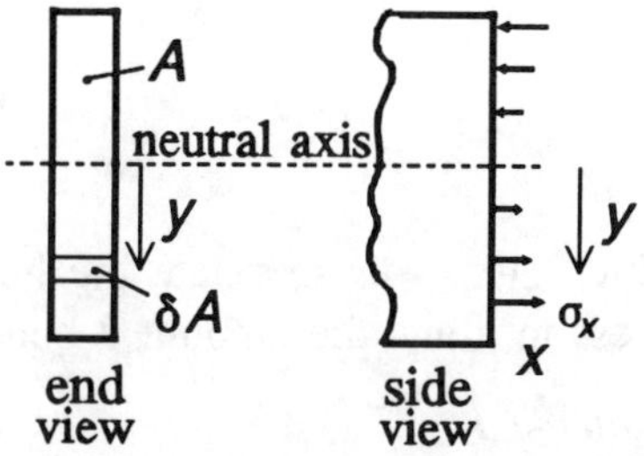

Figure 10.16

The last integral is called the first moment of area about the neutral axis. Any axis about which the first moment of area is zero passes through the *centroid* of the cross section, and vice-versa (see Section 3.3.1 and Appendix II for more discussion of centroids, which are also called *centres of area*).

10.4.1 Bending moments

Although the net axial force in Figure 10.16 is zero, the stress distribution does produce a moment about the neutral axis. This is, of course, the bending moment that the beam carries at this point. By considering the moment of the stress on a small element of area about the neutral axis, we find:

$$M = \int_A \sigma_x y dA$$

and using $\sigma_x = E \epsilon_x = Ey/R$,

$$M = \frac{E}{R} \int_A y^2 dA$$

$$= \frac{EI}{R}$$

where:

$$I = \int_A y^2 dA$$

is the *Second Moment of Area* about the neutral axis (which passes through the centroid), and is a purely geometrical property of the shape (see Appendix II).

Putting all these results together, we obtain the *Bending Formula*:

$$\frac{M}{I} = \frac{E}{R} = \frac{\sigma_x}{y}$$

which allows us to relate the bending moment applied to a beam to both the stress in it and the amount it bends.

Example 1

A rectangular steel beam is 10 mm wide, 20 mm deep and 2 m long. It is simply supported and carries a point load of 200 N at its centre. Calculate the maximum bending stress and minimum radius of curvature in the beam.

Using the bending formula, the minimum radius of curvature will be at the point of maximum bending moment, the centre. The maximum stress will also be at this section, and will be at the maximum distance from the neutral axis. Since this beam is rectangular, the neutral axis is half way down, and the maximum stress will be at the top (compressive) and bottom (tensile).

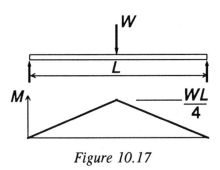

Figure 10.17

$$M_{max} = WL/4 = 100 \text{ N m}$$
(at the centre of the beam)

$$y_{max} = \pm d/2 = \pm 0.01 \text{ m}$$

$$I = bd^3/12 = 0.667 \times 10^{-8} \text{ m}^4$$

$$\therefore \sigma_{max} = \frac{0.01 \times 100}{0.667 \times 10^{-8}} = 150 \text{ MN m}^{-2}$$

(compressive at the top, tensile at the bottom).

The minimum radius of curvature is $R = EI/M_{max} = 13.8 \text{ m}$.

Example 2

The same as Example 1, except that the load of 200 N is uniformly distributed along the length of the beam.

The maximum bending moment is halved compared with the point load case: $M_{max} = 50$ N m. The maximum stress is thus also halved: $\sigma_{max} = 75$ MN m^{-2}, and the radius of curvature is doubled: $R = 27.6$ m.

10.5 SHEAR STRESS

The average shear stress over the section is the shear force Q divided by the area A. This is τ_{xy}, the stress in the y direction on the plane normal to the x axis. There will also be a complementary shear stress τ_{yx} in the horizontal (x) direction. At the top and bottom of the beam, there can be no shear stress, so there must be a maximum near the centre of the beam (in fact, this turns out to be at the neutral axis). The actual distribution of shear stress depends on the cross-sectional shape, but the maximum is usually at most a few times the average.

In most real cases, the shear stresses are much less than the bending stresses. For example, in Example 1 above, the average bending stress is half the maximum, and is given by

$$\sigma_{ave} = \frac{3}{4}\frac{WL}{bd^2}$$

The average shear stress is $Q/A = W/2bd$, so that

$$\frac{\tau_{ave}}{\sigma_{ave}} = \frac{\dfrac{W}{2bd}}{\dfrac{3}{4}\dfrac{WL}{bd^2}} = \frac{2}{3}\frac{d}{L}$$

This will be small so long as the beam is much longer than its depth.

Combined Bending and Shear

The analysis of bending stresses above assumes pure bending, with no shear force or stress. Most real cases have both bending and shear and, in beams, it is not possible to have shear without bending. A full analysis would have to bring shear stresses into the calculation of bending moment, which would complicate things. But as shown above, the shear stresses are usually much lower than the direct bending stresses on average (although on the neutral axis the shear stress is a maximum and the bending stress is zero). The bending formula gives results quite adequate for most purposes so long as it is not asked to predict stresses close to point loads or supports.

More detailed stress analysis identifies shear and direct stresses as different aspects of a more general stress system. Put simply, shear stresses may be considered as direct stresses on planes at 45° to the direction of direct loads. Such analysis is beyond the scope of this book, but is well covered in specialist works.

10.6 DEFLECTION UNDER BENDING

We can use the bending formula to find the deflection of a beam under load. Geometrically, the radius of curvature is related to the slope and second derivative:

$$R = -\frac{\left[1 + \left(\dfrac{dy}{dx}\right)^2\right]^{\frac{3}{2}}}{\dfrac{d^2y}{dx^2}}$$

(the negative sign is needed because we are taking y as positive downwards). In the case of bent beams, the slope is usually very small, so that:

$$\frac{1}{R} = -\frac{d^2y}{dx^2} = \frac{M}{EI}$$

This can be integrated once to give the slope and again to give the deflection.

Example 1

A wooden cantilever 50 mm square in section and 1 m long carries a tip load of 250 N. Calculate its deflected shape and the deflection of its tip.

The bending moment for a tip-loaded cantilever is $M = -W(L - x)$. Therefore:

$$-\frac{d^2y}{dx^2} = \frac{M}{EI} = -\frac{W}{EI}(L - x)$$

Integrating gives:

$$\frac{dy}{dx} = \frac{W}{EI}(Lx - \frac{x^2}{2} + C)$$

and, since the slope at $x = 0$ must be zero, the constant of integration C must be zero.

Integrating again, and noting that the deflection at $x = 0$ is also zero, we obtain the equation of the deflected shape:

$$y = \frac{W}{2EI}x^2(L - \frac{x}{3})$$

This is a cubic curve, with maximum deflection at the tip.

Putting in numbers, $W = 250$ N, E may be taken as 12 GN m^{-2}. With the dimensions given, $I = 52.1 \times 10^{-8}$ m^4. At the tip, $x = 1$ m, the deflection then works out to 13.3 mm.

Example 2

A circular section steel shaft 200 mm *in diameter is mounted in bearings, which may be considered simple supports,* 3 m *apart, and carries a rotor of mass* 400 kg *at its mid point. How much does it deflect under its weight and that of the rotor?*

We will treat the shaft as a uniformly distributed load and the rotor as a point load, calculate the deflections separately and then superpose them.

By integration as above, or from Appendix III, we obtain the central deflection of a uniformly loaded beam as $5wL^4/384EI$. w works out to be 2419 N m^{-1}. For the shaft, $I = \pi d^4/64 = 7.85 \times 10^{-5}$ m^4. Whence for the shaft alone, the central deflection is 1.57×10^{-4} m.

For a beam with a central load, the central deflection is $WL^3/48EI$. This gives a central deflection of 1.36×10^{-4} m due to the rotor. The total deflection is thus 2.93×10^{-4} m, or about 0.3 mm.

Clearly, we can carry out a similar procedure for any other loading and geometry, to find the slope and/or deflection at any desired point. Very often, though, the bending moment is not given by one continuous function (for example it changes slope at point loads). The integrations must be carried out for each section separately, and matched for slope and deflection where they meet to find the constants of integration. Macaulay's notation, described in section 10.2 above, may be used.

Many specific loading and support systems are tabulated in data books. Some simple ones are given in Appendix III. More complicated ones can often be solved by superposition of these.

10.7 DESIGN OF BEAMS

There are two principal criteria in designing beams: the material should not be overstressed, and the deflection should not be excessive. Subject to these, the minimum material should be used.

The bending stress is mostly taken by the extreme top and bottom of the beam. Putting more material at the extremes and less in between will increase the load carrying capacity of the beam (the second moment of area I is increased for a given cross-sectional area or weight). This is the reason for the popular **I** section beam. The horizontal flanges take most of the bending stress, while the vertical web just keeps them correctly positioned and takes the (much smaller) shear stress.

Increasing the depth of a beam increases its stiffness much more than increasing its width. A 2:1 ratio beam is 4 times as stiff on edge as it is flat (since I is proportional to bd^3, and $bd = A$ is constant).

Two beams side by side will be twice as stiff as one, but if *fixed* together on top of each other, they will be 8 times as stiff. But they must be securely fixed - the shear stress on the centre line must be transmitted between them. If they can slide against each other, they will be only twice as stiff as one.

10.8 COMBINED END LOAD AND BENDING

In many situations, a beam will be subject to both a tensile or compressive end load and a bending load. For example, a column (or vertical cantilever) is in compression due to its own weight and any load it supports, but also may be in bending due to either design loads (e.g. overhead electric conductors) or parasitic loads (e.g. wind). Since we are assuming linear stress and strain systems, we can use superposition methods.

Consider a beam of cross-sectional area A (b wide by d deep) which is subject to a tensile end load P and bending loads which produce a linear variation of stress from one side to the other, as above. The total stress at any point will be:

$$\sigma_x = \frac{P}{A} + \frac{My}{I}$$

$$= \frac{P}{bd} + \frac{12My}{bd^3}$$

The stress is still distributed linearly across the depth. However, the maximum tensile stress is increased, while the maximum compressive stress is reduced. If P is large enough, there may actually be no compressive stress. Conversely, if P is negative (compressive end load), we can eliminate tensile stress. This approach is used in pre-stressed composite materials. For example, concrete may be reinforced with steel, with built-in stresses putting the concrete in compression and the steel in tension. Concrete is strong in compression, but very weak in tension. Pre-compressing the concrete (pre-tensioning the steel) avoids it going into tension when bending loads are applied.

We may also note that the neutral axis now no longer passes through the centroid of the cross-section (since $\int_A \sigma_x \, dy \neq 0$). If the stress does not change sign, the neutral axis will not even be inside the cross-section. The bending moment is,however, still given by the moments of the stresses about an axis through the centroid. The uniformly distributed stress from the end load produces no moment about that axis. But if the axial load is not uniformly distributed (or, more generally, the end force does not effectively act at the centroid) it will produce additional bending moments which must be taken into account. Such cases are discussed in detail in specialist books.

EXAMPLES

10.1   A wind generator is mounted on to of an un-stayed vertical pole 25 m high, the bottom of which is built into the ground. The wind force on the generator is 900 N, while that on the pole is 300 N m^{-1}. Find the maximum value of bending moment in the pole, and its position.
(Ans: 116.3 kN m, at base)

10.2   An overhung hollow steel shaft is 50 mm outside diameter and 30 mm inside diameter, and carries a gear wheel of mass 20 kg at a distance 0.5 m from its support (where it may be considered "built in". Calculate (a) the average shear stress in the shaft, (b) the maximum bending stress in the shaft, and (c) the deflection of the centre of the gear wheel.
(Ans: (a) 194.3 kN m^{-2}, (b) 10.32 MN m^{-2}, (c) 0.16 mm)

10.3   The wind generator pole in question 10.1 is a tube 0.3 m outside diameter, 25 mm wall thickness. Calculate the maximum stress in the material. If it is made of aluminium alloy, estimate the tip deflection under the load given.
(Ans: 42.35 MN m^{-2}, 0.68 m)

10.4   A simply supported wooden beam which is 3 m long and of rectangular
        cross-section of area 50 cm^2 carries a point load of 800 N at its mid-
        point. Calculate the minimum depth of the beam if (a) the deflection is
        not to exceed 5 mm, and (b) the maximum stress in the beam is not to
        exceed 20 MN m^{-2}.
        (Ans: (a) 134 mm, (b) 36 mm)

10.5   A wooden distribution pole is 10 m high and 250 mm in diameter. It
        anchors the ends of two copper conductors, which are 90° apart in a
        horizontal plane at the top of the pole. What is the maximum permitted
        tension in the conductors (assumed the same in both) if the stress in the
        pole is not to exceed 50 MN m^{-2}? What diameter should the conductors
        be if the stress in them is not to exceed 150 MN m^{-2}?
        (Ans: 5.42 kN, 6.78 mm)

10.6   A robot arm is made of aluminium tube 30 mm outside diameter and
        20 mm inside diameter. The upper arm and forearm are each 0.75 m
        long. Calculate the vertical deflection of the gripper when the arm
        carries a load of 20 kg, when the arm is fully extended (Figure 10.18a)
        and fully retracted (Figure 10.18b). Neglect any deflection in the joints
        due to the load.

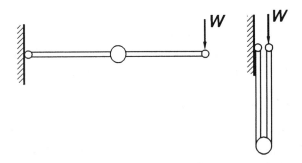

Figure 10.18a   *Figure 10.18b*

(Ans: 99 mm, 11 μm)

10.7   The desk lamp shown in Figure 10.19 has a maximum reach of 1.2 m. The lamp assembly has a mass of 1.5 kg. Calculate the diameter of the vertical swivel pin if the stress in it is not to exceed 100 MN m^{-2}.

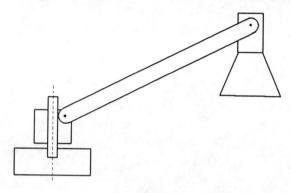

Figure 10.19

(Ans: 12 mm)

10.8   A water channel is made of sheet metal 3 mm thick. The channel cross-section is 450 mm wide and 300 mm deep. It has a simply-supported span of 7 m. Calculate the maximum depth of water it can carry if the maximum stress is not to exceed 40 MN m^{-2}. Ignore the weight of the channel.
(Ans: 213 mm)

11

Torsion

Rotating systems (and some non-rotating ones) are often stressed in *torsion*. Torques (couples, moments) are applied at various positions along a shaft, and transmitted along it by shear stresses. There will be corresponding shear strains, which will result in angular deflections (or twist). For equilibrium in rotation, the total applied couple must be zero. We can approach torsion in a very similar way to bending.

Virtually all practical applications which we are likely to encounter will involve shafts of circular cross-section. This is fortunate, as they are relatively amenable to analysis, while non-circular shafts are not. We will confine ourselves to the former.

11.1 TORQUE DIAGRAMS

A torque diagram shows the variation of torque along a shaft, in a similar way to a shear force diagram on a beam. Figure 11.1 shows an example of a motor driving a shaft with four output torques T_1 to T_4. The motor torque is T_m.

As on the shear force diagram, we can see that torque changes in a stepwise fashion where there is an applied torque (which might be a pulley or gear, a brake, a crank, a cam or an eccentric). It is also possible to have a distributed torque - for example in an electric generator or steam turbine, the torque is transferred to or from the shaft over a significant length. The torque diagram

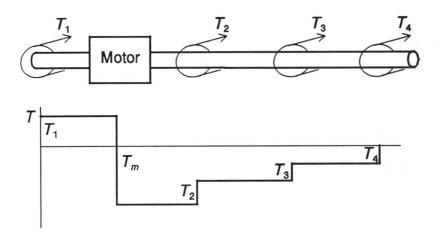

Figure 11.1

will then vary, not necessarily linearly, from one value to the other over this length.

The effect of gearing on torques in shafts has already been discussed in section 8.5.1. By and large, the behaviour is the same whether the shafts are stationary or in steady rotation. In summary, a step-up gear system increases the angle of rotation and rotational speed and reduces the torque in proportion to the gear ratio, and vice-versa.

11.2 SHEAR STRESS AND STRAIN IN CIRCULAR SHAFTS

The torque is transmitted by a distribution of shear stress over the cross-section of the shaft. We will assume circular symmetry, so that at any cross-section, τ is a function only of the radius r.

Let us consider a small element of material, as in Figure 11.2. The shear force on the element is:

$$\tau \delta r r \delta \theta$$

The moment of this force about the axis is an elementary torque:

$$dT = \tau r^2 \delta r \delta \theta$$

and the total torque is:

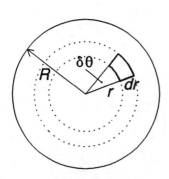

$$T = \int_0^{2\pi} \int_0^R \tau r^2 \, dr \, d\theta$$

Assuming τ is independent of θ, as above:

$$T = 2\pi \int_0^R \tau r^2 \, dr$$

Figure 11.2

Thus if we know the shear stress distribution, we can calculate the torque.

The shear stress distribution may be found by considering the shear strain, in a similar way to that used for bending (Chapter 10). Shear strain is defined as the angle between a line in its original position and in its strained position. Consider a cylinder of material of length L and radius r which, due to a torque T, is twisted through an angle θ (Figure 11.3).

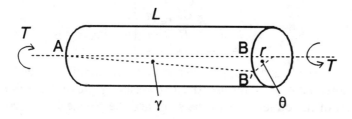

Figure 11.3

AB is a line drawn on the surface initially parallel to the axis. AB' is the same line, after the material has been strained. The angle γ between AB and AB' is the shear strain.

$$\gamma L = r\theta$$

Since at any axial position θ is independent of r, the shear strain varies linearly with radius, just as the direct strain varied linearly with depth for bending.

Assuming a linear elastic material, it follows that the shear stress is also directly proportional to radius:

$$\tau = G\gamma = \frac{Gr\theta}{L}$$

We can now integrate the torque expression above:

$$T = 2\pi \int_0^R \tau r^2 dr = 2\pi \frac{G\theta}{L} \int_0^R r^3 dr$$

$$= \frac{GJ\theta}{L}$$

$$\text{where} \quad J = 2\pi \int_0^R r^3 dr = \int_A r^2 dA$$

J is called the second polar moment of area, and is a property of the shape of the cross-section. For a circular solid shaft, as here, $J = \pi R^4/2 = \pi d^4/32$.

Bringing these results together, we obtain the *Torsion Formula*:

$$\boxed{\frac{T}{J} = \frac{G\theta}{L} = \frac{\tau}{r}}$$

This formula is directly analogous to the bending formula of Chapter 10 (section 10.4.1). It allows us to relate torque, shear stress and angle of deflection (twist), taking account of the dimensions of the shaft and the physical properties of the material.

Example

What diameter is required for a shaft which is to transmit 40 kW at 2 rev s⁻¹, without exceeding either a shear stress of 50 MN m⁻² or a twist of 0.5° m⁻¹? G may be taken as 77 GN m⁻².

Torque: $$T = \frac{\text{power}}{\text{speed}} = \frac{40 \times 10^3}{2 \times 2\pi} = 3183 \text{ N m}$$

(a) Stress:

$$\tau_{max} = \frac{RT}{J} \qquad \therefore \ R = \frac{\tau_{max} J}{T}$$

$$J = \frac{\pi R^4}{2}$$

$$\therefore R = \frac{\tau_{max} \ \pi R^4}{2T}$$

This gives $R = 34.3$ mm, $d = 68.7$ mm as the minimum required to satisfy the stress requirement.

(b) Twist:

$$\frac{T}{J} = \frac{G\theta}{L}, \qquad J = \frac{TL}{G\theta}$$

$$\frac{\pi d^4}{32} = \frac{TL}{G\theta}, \qquad d^4 = \frac{32TL}{\pi G\theta}$$

The minimum diameter to satisfy the twist requirement comes out to 83.3 mm.

The latter diameter is larger, so the twist in the shaft is a more important criterion than the shear stress in this case, and a shaft diameter of 83.3 mm is required.

Example - Torque Meter

Figure 11.4 is a simplified sketch of a widely used device for measuring the torque in a shaft. The torsion bar in the centre is made to suitable dimensions

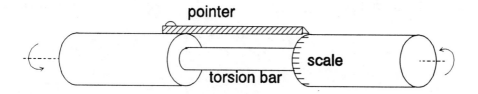

Figure 11.4

for the design torque of the instrument; in some cases it could be the full shaft diameter. The pointer (which may actually be a sleeve) is fixed to the shaft at one end and not at the other, so that it carries no torque. Calibration marks on the shaft and the pointer (or sleeve) move relative to each other as the torsion bar twists under the torque. This movement may be observed using a stroboscope tuned to the rotational speed of the shaft. For remote reading, some form of relative position transducer and telemetry is used.

11.3 TORSION OF A TUBE

The above analysis assumed a solid shaft of outside diameter d. The shear stress is proportional to radius, so that there is no shear stress on the axis, and only low shear stress in the central part of the shaft. For this reason, it is often advantageous to leave out the material in the centre, and transmit the torque using a tube.

The analysis for a tube follows identical lines to that for a shaft, and the same torsion formula is obtained. The only difference is in the value of the polar second moment of area, which now becomes:

$$J = \frac{\pi(R_1^4 - R_2^4)}{2} = \frac{\pi(d_1^4 - d_2^4)}{32}$$

where the suffices 1 and 2 refer to the outer and inner radii and diameters respectively.

Example

Two shafts are to be the same weight. One is to be solid, and the other hollow, with outer diameter twice the inner diameter. Calculate the ratio of torques they can transmit for the same maximum shear stress.

Use suffices s and h to refer to the solid and hollow shafts, respectively. The torques are given by:

$$T_s = \frac{J_s \tau_{max}}{R_s} = \frac{\pi R_s^3 \tau_{max}}{2}$$

$$T_h = \frac{J_h \tau_{max}}{R_h} = \frac{\pi(R_{1h}^4 - R_{2h}^4) \tau_{max}}{2R_{1h}}$$

$R_{1h} = 2R_{2h}$ (given), and $R_s^2 = R_{1h}^2 - R_{2h}^2$ (same cross-sectional area).

$$\therefore \quad \frac{T_h}{T_s} = \frac{5}{2\sqrt{3}} = 1.44$$

The hollow shaft can thus carry 44% more torque than the solid one, for the same amount of material and the same maximum stress. Taking this to extremes, the most efficient shaft is of very large diameter and thin wall, so that all the material carries the maximum stress. However, this may be unreasonably large, and introduces problems of stability against collapse of the tube under point loads, such as bearings, and its own weight.

11.4 THE COIL SPRING

The familiar helical coil spring in fact works in torsion. Figure 11.5 (which is a sketch of one end of a spring) shows that the axial load F is actually carried on a radial cantilever of length R. The resulting bending moment at the root of the cantilever is provided by torque in the spring helix wire. This torque is given by $T = FR$. If the total twist in the wire is θ, this will also be the deflection of the radial cantilever from the horizontal (ignoring bending in the cantilever), so that the spring extension $\delta = R\theta$. (This implicitly assumes that θ and δ are small. This does not cause any problem, however. We can look at a very small portion of the helix, and calculate the deflection of a very short spring. Then we simply add together the deflections of many such short springs - an integration process - to obtain the total deflection.) If the spring is made up of n turns of wire of diameter d, with total wire length $L = 2\pi Rn$, we can use the torsion formula to derive an expression for the spring stiffness $k = F/\delta$:

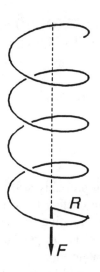

Figure 11.5

$$\theta = \frac{TL}{GJ}$$

$$\theta = \frac{\delta}{R} \quad \text{and} \quad T = FR$$

$$\therefore \quad \frac{\delta}{R} = \frac{(FR)L}{GJ}$$

$$L = 2\pi Rn \quad \text{and} \quad J = \frac{\pi d^4}{32}$$

$$\therefore \delta = \frac{64R^3 n}{Gd^4} F$$

$$\text{and} \quad k = \frac{F}{\delta} = \frac{Gd^4}{64R^3 n}$$

As a numerical example, consider a steel spring ($G = 82$ GN m^{-2}) of 17 mm radius, with wire of 1.65 mm radius, and with 42 turns. The spring stiffness k will be:

$$k = \frac{Gd^4}{64R^3 n} = \frac{82 \times 10^9 \times (1.65 \times 10^{-3})^4}{64 \times (17 \times 10^{-3})^3 \times 42} = 46 \text{ N m}^{-1}$$

11.5 NON-UNIFORM SHAFTS

If the diameter of a shaft varies over its length, we can probably still apply the same methods. The torque will be continuous over the change in section. For gradual changes (such as conical shafts), the arguments relating to shear strain and shear stress will still apply. The angle of twist will no longer be uniform along the shaft, and the total twist must be found by integration.

For sudden changes of section, although the torque will be constant, there will be anomalous stress and strain conditions near the change. The torsion formula will still apply some way away (by St Venant's principle, as discussed in Chapters 3 and 9, above).

As an example, we will consider a shaft consisting of two parts: a length L_1 of diameter d_1, and a length L_2 of diameter d_2 (Figure 11.6). Both parts are made of the same material, and any anomalous behaviour near the change in section is ignored.

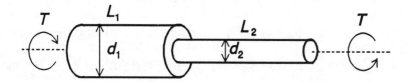

Figure 11.6

The overall twist in the shaft is the sum of the twists in the two parts:

$$\theta = \theta_1 + \theta_2$$

and the torque is the same in both:

$$T = T_1 = T_2$$

Using the torsion formula,

$$\theta_1 = \frac{T}{G}\frac{L_1}{J_1} \qquad\qquad \theta_2 = \frac{T}{G}\frac{L_2}{J_2}$$

$$\therefore \theta = \theta_1 + \theta_2 = \frac{T}{G}\left(\frac{L_1}{J_1} + \frac{L_2}{J_2}\right)$$

Since J is proportional to d^4, the twist per unit length in each shaft is also proportional to d^4. The surface shear stress is proportional to the diameter and inversely proportional to J (from the torsion formula), so that this is proportional to d^3.

EXAMPLES

11.1   A solid steel circular shaft is to be used to transmit 650 MW at 3000 rev min^{-1} over a length of 30 m. Calculate the minimum necessary shaft diameter if the shear stress is not to exceed 80×10^6 N m^{-2}. Calculate also the angle of twist over the length of the shaft, if its diameter is 10% greater than the above minimum.
(Ans: 0.509 m, 4.6°)

11.2 An alternator shaft is to transmit 300 MW at a rotational speed of 750 rev min⁻¹. The maximum shear stress is not allowed to exceed 10^8 N m⁻². Calculate (a) the minimum diameter for a solid shaft; (b) the outside diameter for a hollow shaft whose internal diameter is two-thirds the outside diameter; (c) the angle of twist in a 2 m length of each of the above shafts.

(Ans: (a) 0.579 m, (b) 0.624 m, (c) 0.50° (solid) and 0.46° (hollow))

11.3 Two solid steel shafts are geared together as shown in Figure 11.7. A torque T is applied to the smaller shaft, as shown. Calculate: (a) the angle of twist at the point of application of T, for $T = 10$ N m; (b) the maximum value of T if the shear stress is not to exceed 275 MN m⁻² in either shaft. Assume a shear modulus of 80 GN m⁻², and ignore deflection of the gear teeth.

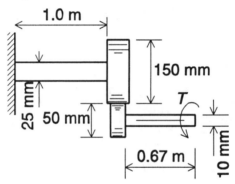

Figure 11.7

(Ans: (a) 6.88°, (b) $T = 54$ N m due to smaller shaft (larger could take $T = 281$ N m))

11.4 A nylon spindle consists of a solid portion of length 0.75 m, diameter 25 mm, attached to a hollow portion of length 0.5 m, outside diameter 25 mm, inside diameter 20 mm. A torque of 5 N m is transmitted by the spindle. What is the angle of twist in each part? (Take the shear modulus of nylon as 1 GN m⁻².)

(Ans: Solid part 5.6°, hollow part 6.3°)

11.5 Two shafts of the same material but different diameters are fixed together at point B, as shown in Figure 11.8. Ends A and C are fixed so that they cannot rotate. A torque M is applied at B. Find the restraining torques necessary at A and B.

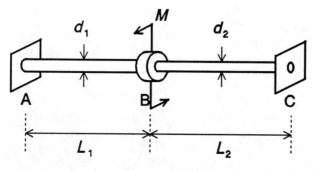

Figure 11.8

If the two shafts were different materials, what ratio would their shear moduli have to have in order to make the torques at A and B equal?

$$\left(T_A = M\frac{L_2 d_1^4}{L_1 d_2^4 + L_2 d_1^4}, \quad T_B = M\frac{L_1 d_2^4}{L_1 d_2^4 + L_2 d_1^4}, \quad \frac{G_1}{G_2} = \frac{L_2 d_2^4}{L_1 d_1^4}\right)$$

11.6 A torsion spring consists of a steel bar A of diameter 18 mm, length 300 mm, concentrically fixed inside a steel tube B of inside diameter 20 mm, outside diameter 25 mm and length 250 mm, as shown in Figure 11.9. Calculate the torsional spring stiffness.

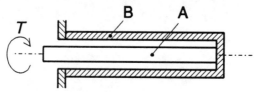

Figure 11.9

(Ans: 2274 N m rad^{-1})

12

Material Properties

Up to this point, we have made very simple assumptions about the properties of the materials we have been dealing with: we have generally assumed them to be linear elastic and isotropic. Real materials, however, are never so simple. At the best, they have properties which approximate to our ideal over a certain range of stress and strain. In this chapter, we will consider the accuracy and range of this approximation for some common materials. Actual numerical values are given in Appendix IV.

12.1 TENSILE TESTING

A common and useful way of measuring and displaying the properties of a material is the tensile test. A suitably shaped specimen of the material (often a bar or rod) is subjected to a steadily increasing load (usually using a hydraulic jacking system) , and its length is measured. From this, the average stress and strain can be calculated, and stress plotted against strain. The test is often continued until the specimen breaks. A variant on this is to apply a known distortion (strain) (perhaps with a screw jack), and measure the stress required.

12.1.1 Metals

Figure 12.1 shows a typical stress/strain characteristic for a mild steel. At low strains (A to B), the curve is substantially linear. The behaviour is elastic. Then

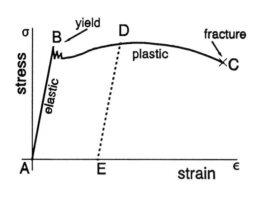

Figure 12.1

at point B, there is a change in behaviour - the strain suddenly increases, while the stress falls somewhat. This is called the *yield point*, and the corresponding stress and strain values are the yield stress and strain. The yield point may also be called the *elastic limit*. After point B, the strain increases enormously with little change in stress. This is the *plastic region*. Eventually, at point C, the specimen breaks. The stress at fracture is called the *Ultimate Tensile Strength* (UTS). Although the stress may appear to fall in the plastic region, this is an artefact. As the specimen deforms, its cross-sectional area decreases, and the stress for a given load increases. Figure 12.1 is drawn using *nominal stress* - the stress obtained by dividing the load by the original area. If instead, *true stress* is used, allowing for the reduction of area, the curve rises steadily throughout the plastic region (although there is still a dip at the yield), and the failure occurs at the highest true stress level reached. The measurement of cross-sectional area is not particularly easy, and nominal stress is conventionally used in most cases.

In the elastic range AB, if the load is removed, the same line is retraced in reverse. In the plastic region BC, however, if the load is removed at point D, the strain relaxes along a line such as DE to produce a permanent plastic distortion AE, the *permanent set*. Re-applying the load, the stress will retrace ED and then DC, to fail at the same point. The behaviour of a particular specimen therefore depends on its history of previous loading. A newly annealed (heat treated to restore its original properties) specimen will have a lower yield stress than one which has been loaded beyond the yield and back. This phenomenon is called *strain hardening*.

The strain at the elastic limit is relatively small compared to that at fracture - of the order of 0.1% and 50% respectively. A material with properties like this is described as *ductile*. For such a material, the yield stress is usually taken as the maximum permitted stress for design purposes, although there are techniques which make use of redundancy to allow stresses to rise above the yield into the plastic region without undue strain. The yield stress is significantly affected by temperature, particularly below normal ambient temperatures.

By contrast, Figure 12.2 shows the typical stress/strain curve for cast iron. There is no yield or plastic region, failure happens abruptly in the elastic region,

and the characteristic is usually substantially
linear right up to failure. The strain at failure
might be 0.3%. A material which behaves
like this is said to be *brittle*. Many non-
metallic materials also show brittle behaviour.
Examples are ceramics, crystalline solids and
glasses at low temperature.

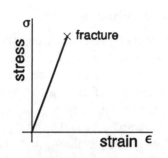

Figure 12.2

Some materials, in particular steels,
undergo a transition from ductile to brittle
behaviour as the temperature is reduced. The
transition temperature can easily be within the
range of normal operation in cold climates. Special consideration has to be given
to materials which may be used at low temperature.

Not all metals exhibit yielding behaviour.
Figure 12.3 shows the shape of the stress-
strain curve for a metal such as soft copper or
aluminium. Although it may be approximated
as linear at low stress, it is in fact
continuously curving. When unloaded, it
follows a different curve back to zero stress,
leaving permanent set. To produce the same
strain again from this point, a higher stress is
needed. Taking the metal through a cycle of
loading and unloading effectively makes it
stronger - the phenomenon of *work
hardening*. The original properties may be
restored by *annealing* - a heat treatment
process which restores the original crystal structure within the material.

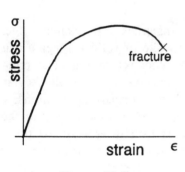

Figure 12.3

If there is no yield point, some other criterion is needed for the limit of the
approximately linear region or the maximum permitted stress. The *elastic limit*
and *proof stress* are defined as those stresses which produce some specified value
of permanent set. For example, 0.1% or 0.2% proof stress may be used.

12.1.2 Ceramics and glasses

Ceramic and glass materials usually show elastic/brittle behaviour, in a similar
way to cast iron. Glasses, however, are susceptible to *creep*: an increase of
strain with time, at constant stress. This is particularly the case at elevated
temperatures. Their behaviour is often described as *visco-elastic*. Over short
time scales, they have brittle/elastic properties. Over long time scales, they flow
like a highly viscous fluid (tar or treacle). Metals may also creep, but in general
the time scales required are much longer than for glasses.

12.1.3 Polymers

Polymers ("plastics") are generally also visco-elastic. They may be brittle at low temperatures, but often have complex plastic extension behaviour at normal temperatures, and very pronounced creep behaviour. This may be combined with a memory effect - after apparently deforming plastically and acquiring a permanent set, they may slowly relax back towards their original state - a kind of reversed creep. The yield is often very pronounced with polymers - when inflating a toy balloon, it is often neccessary to blow very hard to get it started (through the yield), then much easier to blow it up to a larger size (through the plastic region). When deflated, it does not return to the original size (permanent set). All properties are strongly temperature dependent. There are a very large number of different polymers, with an enormous range of properties. Expert advice is always needed if they are to be used under stress.

12.1.4 Composites

Composites are combinations of two or more materials: for example steel reinforced concrete (concrete itself being a composite of solid aggregate and cement binder) and glass reinforced plastic (GRP). Wood is a naturally occurring composite. In recent years, many metal based composites (for example, kevlar reinforced aluminium alloy) have been developed for aerospace applications.

Composites are often anisotropic. Their properties vary according to the direction being measured. For example, wood is usually at least 20 times stronger along the grain than across it. Such properties can be put to excellent use by structural designers to provide maximum strength at the positions and in the directions needed, while minimising weight by not providing strength where it is not needed.

Composites, like most materials, usually have a linear elastic range at low stress levels. They then have a complex pattern of stress/strain behaviour, often with several yields. The yielding processes are usually irreversible, since they involve loss of adhesion between the components or breaking of the reinforcing fibres. Failure usually involves tearing of reinforcement out of the matrix.

12.2 COMPRESSION

Compression testing can be carried out in a similar manner to tensile testing. Within the elastic range, behaviour is very similar, and the slope of the graph (Young's modulus) is close to the same value. The elastic limit also occurs at much the same value.

Ductile materials undergo plastic deformation in compression, but for a variety of practical reasons, the characteristics are not particularly easy to measure, and depend very much on the specimen size and shape. There is no equivalent of the UTS. Many materials can be deformed plastically in compression virtually without limit. This fact is put to excellent use in such forming processes as rolling and forging.

Brittle failure does not occur in compression in the same way as in tension. Brittle materials loaded in compression usually fail in shear on planes at 45° to the load. For example, when a concrete block is loaded in compression, flakes break off the edges and corners progressively until the whole block is reduced to a heap of small pieces.

For materials such as concrete which have very little tensile strength, properties have to be measured in compression. Standardized test blocks and testing methods must be used for comparison and quality control, but the results of these are often difficult to relate back to material properties.

12.3 TORSION

Torsion testing is complicated by the fact that the shear stress across the cross section is not constant (see Chapter 11, section 11.2). Obtaining material shear stress/shear strain properties is not difficult while all the material is in the elastic range, but as soon as part of it (at the outer radius) enters the plastic range, problems occur.

Ductile materials in torsion can sustain very high values of shear strain before failing (perhaps several hundred percent), and fail in shear on a plane at right angles to the torque. Brittle materials accept far less strain, and fail on planes at 45° to the axis, producing a helical geometry at the broken face. Yield stresses and ultimate strengths in shear are usually rather lower than in tension, often around 50-60%.

12.4 HARDNESS

Hardness is a property of a material closely related to its strength. It determines the susceptibility of the material to surface damage such as scratching, abrasion or indentation. It also affects the machinability of the material and, to some extent, its resistance to wear. Hardness cannot be determined directly from bulk tests, however, since material near the surface often has rather different properties to the average. This can arise from various effects:

- processes such as machining or grinding can cause local work hardening;
- the chemical composition near the surface can differ due to oxidation or inclusion of "foreign" material;
- the surface of a casting cools faster than the interior, giving different properties;

- the surface may be deliberately modified by heat treatment or case hardening techniques.

Hardness is measured by a number of different (and not altogether compatible) standardized techniques, usually involving applying a local concentrated load and measuring the size of the indentation produced. Common tests are the Brinell test, using a hardened steel ball, the Vickers test, using a diamond pyramid, and the Rockwell test using either a diamond cone or a steel ball. Each of these produces a *hardness number*, but converting between the different tests, and comparison with tensile strengths, is at best approximate. The Details of the test used must always be provided with the test results.

13

Failure and its Avoidance

The primary aim of the engineer is to make things that work. Secondary aims involve considerations such as cost, appearance, efficiency, environmental effects, etc. In order to reach a satisfactory compromise between conflicting requirements, it is essential to know what might go wrong, and how likely it is to do so.

13.1 WHAT IS FAILURE?

What do we mean by "failure", and how do we know when a component or structure has "failed"? The most rational definition is "when it no longer carries out its assigned job". This assumes that we know what it is meant to do, which is not always the case. One of the principle aims of engineering design is to define exactly what every component should do, but this is rarely achieved. If we are not certain what it should do, we may not be able to decide whether it still does it or not. The problem arises because few components have only one rôle. An overhead electrical conductor has a primary function of carrying an electrical current. But it is also required to carry the stresses induced by its own weight, tension and other factors such as wind or ice. Further, it must dissipate the heat generated by resistive effects, perform adequately under a wide range of weather conditions, maintain adequate clearance between itself and other conductors, towers, the ground, and other nearby structures, and stay attached to its supports. If any of these (or a host of others) are unsatisfactory, the conductor has failed. All these even without consideration of first cost, maintenance, environmental effects, visual appearance, and so on.

With the best will in the world, there will always be failures. Sometimes, these will be as a result of a calculated risk on the part of the designer. For example, our overhead conductor might have a design life of 20 years, and be designed to withstand a wind which statistically occurs only once in 100 years. If such a wind occurred, and it might at any time, the conductor might fail. The cost of designing for a higher and rarer wind speed must be traded against the probability and cost of a failure. At other times, failures may occur through events which, realistically, are quite unforeseeable. The designer of a transmission line cannot be expected to take military activity into account, nor to consider the possibility of some future railway tunnel passing under the line. Yet both these could cause failure. (In the latter case, of course, the railway engineer should consider the transmission line passing over the projected route.)

The consequences of failure may range from the trivial to the catastrophic. The balance between design and cost will depend on the potential seriousness of the outcome. If this is likely to be extreme, as in the nuclear industry, the design must take account of extremely unlikely scenarios, and the cost will escalate rapidly. If the repercussions are minimal, then greater uncertainties and risks can be taken.

One way of minimising the seriousness of a failure is to use a *fail-safe* design. This does not mean that failure will cause no problem - by definition, it always does. Rather, it means that the consequences are reduced to the minimum for that particular failure. As a trivial example, consider overload protection of an electrical circuit. If the protection device (fuse or circuit breaker) is put in the neutral line, although current will cease to flow when the failure occurs, high voltages will still be present. If the fuse is in the live line, this will not be the case. Protecting both lines would, at first sight, appear safer than just protecting one. However, this is not so: it is unlikely that both would trip simultaneously, and we could be left with an unsafe system with the live still connected.

Fail-safe systems can either be *passive*, where the failure itself results in a relatively safe situation, or *active*, where a protection system senses the failure and takes appropriate action. All such systems usually rely on redundancy in their design. An example of a passive system is the vacuum brakes used on railways. The brakes are normally on, and have to be held off against a spring system by (negative) air pressure. If the vacuum system fails, the brakes are applied by the spring. This is only fail-safe if the spring does not fail. However, there is usually a spring on every wheel, but only one vacuum system. The system is protected against spring failure by redundancy. Active fail-safe is used on aircraft, spacecraft and nuclear installations. All aspects of the system behaviour are monitored by computer, and appropriate action taken if a fault is detected. However, this approach rapidly increases in complexity as extra systems have to be provided to protect against failure in the protection system, and so on. The US space shuttles use a redundancy system with three computers, from different manufacturers and programmed by different teams, working in parallel. Decisions are taken by majority voting of the three computers. This reduces, but does not eliminate, the possibility of protection system failure.

In this chapter, we will only consider failure modes which are directly associated with the stress in the component, while remembering that there are many other considerations to be taken into account in a real design situation. In structural mechanics, passive fail-safe is normally used. The simplest method is to use redundant structures, where the load lost by a failing member is taken up by other members. But a failure sensing system (e.g. regular visual inspection) is still needed to ensure repair before another member fails, and the structure collapses.

13.2 MODES OF STRUCTURAL FAILURE

A component under stress can fail to carry out its design function in a number of ways:

- Excessive Elastic Deformation
- Plastic Deformation
- Permanent Set, arising from earlier Plastic Deformation
- Creep
- Fracture

The first three of these are fairly rapidly dealt with. Excessive elastic deformation may arise from design errors. As we saw in some of the examples in Chapter 10, acceptable elastic deformation often involves stresses much lower than the material yield stresses. It is up to the designer to appreciate this point in any given case. Alternatively, it may arise from overloading. The solution is either to prevent the user from overloading the structure, or make it stiffer. Similarly with plastic deformation: the problem is why the structure was overloaded. Permanent set only arises from earlier abuse.

Creep can lead to a structure changing its shape or size over time. For most materials at moderate loads and temperatures, it is not usually a problem.

Fracture is another matter. There are a number of situations in which fracture may occur other than the obvious one of the ultimate strength being exceeded.

13.2.1 Brittle Fracture

We saw in Chapter 12 that some materials may be brittle under some conditions, particularly at low temperatures. Brittle materials are more susceptible to fail under shock loading than are ductile materials. In an impact, there will be very high transient local stresses near the point of impact. In a ductile material, local plastic deformation will occur, which has the effect of distributing the load and reducing the stress. So long as the whole component does not enter the plastic region, there will be no overall deformation (if it does, energy will be dissipated). In a brittle material, however, a crack is likely to form near the point of impact. This *increases* the local stress both due to reduction of cross-sectional area and stress concentration effects (see Section 13.2.2 below). The crack is likely to extend rapidly right across the component.

Brittle fracture can be avoided by:

(a) Not using brittle materials, or avoiding low temperatures with certain materials. This is the best approach, but is rarely absolutely practicable.

(b) Avoiding shock loading. This is the most common approach where the use of brittle materials is unavoidable (e.g. windows and wine glasses);

(c) Preventing the crack from growing. This is really a way of forcing a fail-safe condition, rather than avoiding fracture. A good example of this is in the use of mild steel, which may become brittle at low temperatures, for construction of ships. If the plates are welded together, a crack can propagate from one plate to the next. There have been instances of ships breaking completely in half in arctic waters. On the other hand, if the plates are riveted, the crack may arrive at a joint and not transfer to the next plate. The two halves of the broken plate are held in position by the redundancy of the structure, and the failure has been in a relatively safe manner.

13.2.2 Stress Concentrations

In calculating stresses, we have usually assumed that they are either uniformly distributed over the cross-sectional area of a component, or that they vary in some well-behaved and understood manner. Unfortunately, this is generally not true. Particularly near changes of section or shape or where loads are applied, stresses are likely to be non-uniform. Since the average stress must be the same, there must be higher stresses than predicted in some places. These are called stress concentrations.

The detailed analysis of stress distributions near discontinuities is extremely complex. However, it is usually possible either theoretically or experimentally to define a *stress concentration factor* for a particular geometrical feature. This is the ratio of the maximum stress on a cross-section to the average stress. Its value generally lies between 1 and 3. For example, for a flat plate in tension, with a circular hole of diameter equal to half the plate width on the centre line, the stress concentration factor is about 2.2 (this is relative to the average stress after allowing for the hole, which is of course already double the average stress far away from the hole). The maximum stress is at the circumference of the hole, at the point of minimum cross section.

As well as increasing local stress, stress concentrations provide a starting point for cracks to grow - for example in brittle materials as above, or in fatigue (Section 13.2.3 below). This can be put to good practical use. Glass is cut by scratching its surface and then applying shock loads. The scratch provides a stress concentration for the crack to start, thus ensuring that the fracture follows the scratched line. Similarly, the holes in perforated paper produces stress concentrations causing it to tear as desired.

Generally, stress concentrations are more severe when the radius of curvature is smaller. For the shaft shown in Figure 11.6 (Chapter 11), there is a severe stress concentration at the change of section, where the radius of curvature is (ideally) zero. The stress concentration factor might be 3 or more. If a fillet was put into the corner to increase the radius of curvature to 30% of the smaller diameter, the stress concentration factor would be reduced to around 1.2. These values are for torsion; similar values would apply in bending. Generally, both bending and torsion will be present. For example, the shaft might be on a motor with a reduction in diameter where the pulley (subject to a side load and torque) is mounted.

Other common sources of stress concentration are holes, keyways, splines, gear teeth and screw threads. Even minor surface defects, scratches, rust or corrosion spots may be enough to cause problems. It is probably true to say that the majority of structural failures occur at stress concentrations, even when the existence of the concentration was not the primary cause of the failure.

13.2.3 Fatigue

Some materials will fail well below their ultimate strength (as given by a tensile test) when they are subject to a repeated alternating load. It is common practice to break thin wire or metal plate by repeatedly bending it to and fro. After a number of cycles (a few tens, perhaps), it breaks, although the maximum stress has been much less than that needed to break it in tension. This is called *fatigue*.

Fatigue occurs because of crack initiation at stress concentrators. Even if there are no major changes in shape or section, minute local surface defects may be enough to initiate it. According to the load and the material characteristics, these minute cracks may grow progressively at each loading cycle. Eventually a crack reaches a critical length at which it becomes unstable and grows extremely rapidly; the component breaks. The number of cycles of loading (the *fatigue life*) needed can vary very much with the conditions and the type of material, from a few cycles to many hundreds of millions. It is essentially a statistical phenomenon; repeated measurements under nominally identical conditions give significant variations in fatigue life. Consequently, the ability to predict fatigue life is also subject to statistical uncertainties.

The life (in time) of a component obviously depends on both its fatigue life (in cycles) and the frequency of the loading. Quite a short life in cycles may be quite acceptable for a component which is loaded and unloaded only rarely (e.g. weekly or annually). On the other hand, rotating machinery may be loaded many hundreds or thousands of times per second, and a long fatigue life is essential.

In general, fatigue life increases as the stress is reduced. For some materials (particularly steels) there is a limiting stress below which the fatigue life is effectively infinite. This might be of the order of 50% of the ultimate strength, and is called the *fatigue limit*. It arises because the internal structure of the

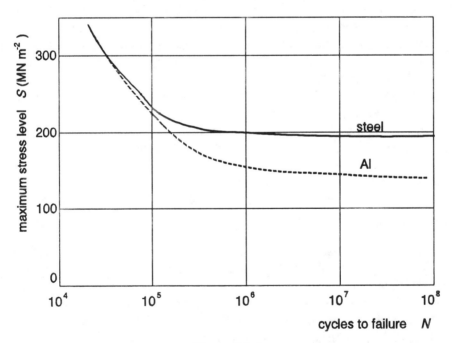

Figure 13.1

material contains non-uniformities which prevent crack propagation below certain stress levels. Other materials, such as non-ferrous metals, have no fatigue limit, and will eventually fail even at very low stress values. Typical fatigue properties of a mild steel and an aluminium alloy are shown on the *S-N curves* in Figure 13.1. The fatigue properties of materials with no fatigue limit are specified by the stress (the *endurance*) at which the life will be some specified number of cycles, often 5×10^7. Statistical methods must be used: the endurance might be defined as the stress level at which 50% of specimens would survive the specified number of cycles.

While the basic mechanism of fatigue is well understood, predictions of fatigue life are not at all easy. Statistical methods with adequate safety factors must be used, and appropriate design precautions such as minimising stress concentrations and avoiding alternating loads taken. Further, incipient fatigue is almost impossible to detect; visual inspection will reveal no abnormalities until just before failure occurs. In safety-critical components made of materials with no fatigue limit (such as aerospace components), the only safe approach is regular replacement of apparently perfect components on a cycles/duration basis.

Fatigue is responsible for many in-service failures. In many cases the results have been catastrophic. For example in the Comet airliner tragedies of the 1950s, fatigue in the aluminium alloy aircraft skin occurred, starting at stress concentrations at the corners of the cabin windows. In others, such as failure of the plastic flexure hinges on sandwich boxes, they are merely inconvenient. Any designer of load bearing components subject to cyclic loading must be aware of the possibility of fatigue.

13.3 SAFETY FACTORS

All the calculation methods we have discussed in the last few chapters have been approximate. They have assumed linear materials of accurately known properties. They have assumed uniformly or linearly distributed stresses. They have assumed perfect workmanship and operation under ideal conditions. None of these is valid, so that none of the predictions will be absolutely correct. Our mathematical models are highly simplified.

As discussed earlier, some of our assumptions are pessimistic. Idealized joints will generally produce higher stresses than more realistic rigid joints. Point loads also produce higher stresses than distributed loads. If we use stress concentration factors appropriate to pin joints or point loads, our design should err on the safe side. Conversely, there are many uncertainties associated with stress concentrations, material properties, fatigue, loading systems, operation, maintenance, wear and tear, etc. which may well work against us. We cannot be sure that our overall design will be safe throughout its specified life.

While we will allow for as many of these factors as possible, as accurately as possible, there will always be uncertainty. It is usual to apply an extra factor, the *safety factor*, to the predicted stresses, to allow for any remaining unknowns.

The size of the safety factor depends on how accurate we believe the estimates to be, how safety-critical the application is, how sensitive the particular materials/applications are to errors, what is the cost (in money, resources or performance) of increasing it, and so on. Quite often, some of these criteria may be in conflict.

In normal engineering applications, safety factors for structures with steady loads might be between 5 and 10. For shock loading and brittle materials, they might be increased to 20 or more. For weight critical applications where extremely sophisticated design methods are available (e.g. aerospace), they might be reduced to 2, 1.5, or less.

It is important that safety factors be correctly applied. In the early 1960s a number of cooling towers collapsed at Ferrybridge Power Station in Yorkshire. The reasons for this were many and complex, but one of them was the application of safety factors. The concrete towers were subject to compressive stress due to weight, and bending stress due to wind loading. On the upwind side, the bending stresses would be tensile. It was essential that they were less than the compressive stresses, to avoid the concrete going into tension. The net stress (which was fairly small) was calculated and an apparently reasonable safety factor applied to it, to be used for the design. Unfortunately, the uncertainty in the wind loading was such as to completely overcome the safety factor, and the concrete went into tension. A safety factor should have been applied to the wind loading (and another, probably smaller, one to the weight), before the net stress was calculated.

Applying the appropriate safety factors to all the various components is one of the most important skills in obtaining an efficient and safe design. Safety factors to be used can only be found from accumulated experience. For many applications, this is summarized in standards, codes of practise and designers' handbooks.

AND FINALLY....

To solve any problem, particularly where a fault or failure has occurred, it is essential to understand how the system is meant to work, and what has gone wrong with it. There are many examples of well-meaning attempts to solve structural problems which have failed due to mis-understanding of the true problem. One is a wooden mediaeval roof structure recently found to be unsafe. It was repaired by removing some Victorian iron "strengthening" members, allowing the load to be carried by the wooden members originally intended, rather than being diverted through the iron into weaker members. Another, described in some detail by Gordon* involved an aircraft which suffered wing failure. Strengthening one of the wing spars made the problem worse, as it made the wing deform elastically in a different manner. Weakening the same spar cured the problem.

The structural engineer is only one of several professionals employed in any project. Yet it is his or her skill which eventually shows. If the accountant gets it wrong, people may lose their jobs or the firm go out of business. If the architect gets it wrong, people will complain about its appearance. If the lawyer gets it wrong, there may be doubt about who owns it or has a right to use it. If the planner gets it wrong, nobody might want to use it. But if the engineer gets it wrong, there will at best be nothing, and at worst a disaster.

---

* Gordon JE, *Structures, or Why Things Don't Fall Down*. Penguin, 1978, p261 *et seq*

Appendix I

Moments of Inertia

I.1 CENTRE OF MASS

The centre of mass G of a solid body is a point defined by the equation:

$$M\mathbf{r}_G = \int_M \mathbf{r}\, dm$$

where M is the total mass of the body, $\mathbf{r}$ is the position vector of an element of mass dm and $\mathbf{r}_G$ is the position vector of G. If the origin for the position vector is coincident with G, the integral, the *first moment of mass about* G, is zero. It can be shown that in statics or linear motion a solid body behaves as if all its mass were concentrated at the centre of mass, and all forces acted there (see Chapter 3, section 3.1.1). Gravitational attraction is such a force, so that the centre of mass is coincident with the *centre of weight* or *centre of gravity*.

The position of the centre of mass can be found by integration, using the definition, or by equilibrium. If a body can be supported at the centre of mass, there is no moment of weight about that point, and the body will be in equilibrium in any orientation. This is not usually possible in practise. However, if a body is suspended from any point, it will hang in equilibrium with the centre of mass vertically below the point of suspension, giving a line which must pass through G. Suspending it from another point, not on that line, will give another line; G is at the intersection of the two lines.

For bodies *made of material of constant density*, the centre of mass will coincide with the *centroid* (see Appendix II). If the body also has symmetries, it will lie on the planes of symmetry. Examples are a sphere, a cylinder, a cone, and many more complex shapes. Other examples are given in Appendix II.

For more complex shapes, and bodies with various parts of different density, it is often possible to find the centres of mass of the separate parts. Then treat them as concentrated masses at their respective centres of mass, and find the resulting centre of mass of the combination.

The centre of mass does not necessarily lie within the boundaries of the body. For example the centre of mass of a hemispherical cup will be in the cup. Depending on the thickness of the cup, it may or may not be within the material.

I.2 MOMENT OF INERTIA

The Moment of Inertia was introduced in Chapter 8. For a solid body, the moment of inertia I_{xx} about an axis xx is defined by:

$$I_{xx} = \int_M r^2 \, dm$$

where r is the radius of mass element *dm* from the axis xx. An alternative name for moment of inertia is *Second Moment of Mass*. It is analagous to the variance of a statistical distribution or the mean square value of a waveform:- it gives a measure of the energy of a system which arises from the distribution of the quantity concerned (mass, in this case) about the mean.

The moments of inertia of two bodies may be added linearly *provided they are both referred to the same axis*. This provides a way of determining the moments of inertia of complex shapes, by adding or subtracting simpler ones.

The *radius of gyration, k,* is defined by:

$$k^2 = \frac{I}{M}$$

and may be considered as a kind of typical radius of the mass distribution. It is analagous to the standard deviation of a statistical distribution or the root mean square of a waveform. One advantage of using radius of gyration rather than moment of inertia is that it is rather more general. For example, the radius of gyration of a uniform thin disk about its axis of symmetry is the same as that of a uniform thick disk, a short cylinder or an infinitely long cylinder.

I.2.1 Parallel Axes Theorem

The moment of inertia I_{xx} (or radius of gyration k_{xx}) about any axis xx may be calculated from that I_{GG} about a parallel axis GG through the centre of mass, using the parallel axes theorem (which is derived in Chapter 8):

$$I_{xx} = I_{GG} + Md^2 \qquad \text{or} \qquad k_{xx}^2 = k_{GG}^2 + d^2$$

where d is the distance between the two axes. It follows from this that I_{xx} is always less than I_{GG}.

This theorem is invaluable. The results of a single calculation or measurement of the moment of inertia about an axis through the centre of mass can be tabulated and used to find that about any parallel axis.

I.2.1 Perpendicular Axes Theorem

In certain circumstances, it is also possible to relate moments of inertia about axes which are perpendicular to each other. Consider an elementary mass dm at a point (x,y,z). Its elementary moments of inertia about the three axes are:

$$dI_{xx} = (y^2 + z^2)dm \qquad dI_{yy} = (z^2 + x^2)dm \qquad dI_{zz} = (x^2 + y^2)dm$$

$$\therefore \quad dI_{xx} + dI_{yy} = (x^2 + y^2 + 2z^2)dm$$
$$= dI_{zz} + 2z^2 dm$$

If there is no mass outside the xy plane (i.e. the body is a lamina), the last term on the right is zero ($dm = 0$ for all non-zero z). Then $dI_{zz} = dI_{xx} + dI_{yy}$. This is not often directly applicable, since bodies are never truly infinitely thin. But it is useful in deriving other results. For example, the radius of gyration a uniform elliptical lamina about its major diameter ($2a$) is readily found by integration to be $a^2/4$. Similarly about its minor axis ($2b$), $b^2/4$. The perpendicular axes theorem then gives us the radius of gyration of the lamina about an axis through its centre and perpendicular to its plane: $I = (a^2 + b^2)/4$. Since an elliptical cylinder is a stack of such laminae, this is also the radius of gyration of an elliptical cylinder about its axis.

I.3 CALCULATION METHODS

For cases where the density is not uniform, it is not practicable to provide specific formulae. Every individual case must be treated separately. If the body is composed of sub-sections which are of uniform density, then these subsections should be analysed individually, and combined (using the parallel axes theorem if appropriate). If the density varies in a continuous manner, then the integration has to be carried out for the particular case concerned.

When the density is uniform, it may be removed from the integration. The calculation of radius of gyration of a lamina then becomes mathematically identical to the equivalent calculation for Second Moment of Area, and the methods of Appendix II may be used. The moment of inertia of the solid may then be obtained by integration of laminae, as appropriate.

Appendix II

Second Moments of Area

II.1 CENTRE OF AREA

The Centre of Area of a shape is a geometrical property, and does not depend
on the material, etc. The centre of area is the same as the *centroid* (which term
is also used for the equivalent three dimensional property, the centre of volume).

For doubly symmetrical shapes, the centroid G is at the point where the axes
of symmetry cross:

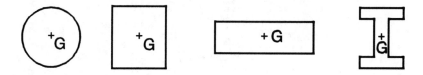

For shapes with one axis of symmetry, it will be on that axis. The actual
position can be found by integration:

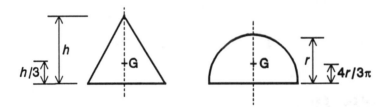

The positions of the centroids of many shapes appear in data and reference books and manufacturers' data sheets. They can always be found by integration, although for irregular shapes graphical or numerical methods may be needed.

Example: A trapezium

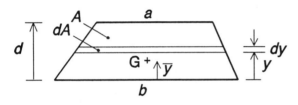

Taking the origin at the bottom edge, the position of the centroid is obtained by taking moments of area:

$$\int_A y\, dA = \bar{y} A$$

(by definition). In this case,

$$A = \left[\frac{a+b}{2}\right] d \qquad \text{and} \qquad dA = \left[b - (b-a)\frac{y}{d}\right] dy$$

The first moment is thus given by:

$$\int_A y\, dA = \int_0^d y \left[b - (b-a)\frac{y}{d}\right] dy$$

$$= d^2 \left[\frac{a}{3} + \frac{b}{6}\right]$$

so that

$$\bar{y} = \frac{1}{A}\int_A y\, dA = \frac{d}{3}\frac{2a+b}{a+b}$$

Notice that if $a = 0$ (triangle), this reduces to $d/3$, as above. If $a = b$ (rectangle), it gives $d/2$.

Complicated shapes can often be made up from simpler ones:

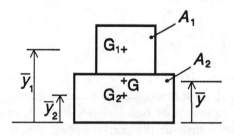

Taking moments about the base line:

$$\bar{y}(A_1 + A_2) = \bar{y}_1 A_1 + \bar{y}_2 A_2$$

II.2 SECOND MOMENTS OF AREA

The second moment of area of a shape about an axis lying in its plane is a property of the shape and the position and direction of the axis alone, independent of the material. It is always positive (and non-zero). It is defined by:

$$I_{xx} = \int_A y^2 dA$$

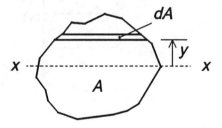

where the y is the distance from the axis xx. It is always necessary to specify the axis about which the moment is calculated. In general, the second moment about one axis will be different from that about another.

In calculating bending stresses, we nearly always want the second moment about the neutral axis - i.e. the axis through the centroid. This is usually designated by I_G or I_O, or often just by I alone. If we do require that about some other axis, we can use the *parallel axes theorem*:

$$I_{xx} = I_G + \bar{y}^2 A$$

where $\bar{y}$ is the distance between the axis through the centroid G and a parallel axis xx, and A is the area. The derivation of this theorem is similar to that given in Chapter 8 for the equivalent theorem for moments of inertia. It can be seen that the second moment about an axis through the centroid is the smallest possible for any of the parallel axes. We can also use the *perpendicular axes theorem*:

$$I_{zz} = I_{xx} + I_{yy}$$

where xx and yy are mutually perpendicular axes in the plane of the area, and zz is the axis perpendicular to both of them through their point of intersection. This is useful for establishing polar moments of area (see Section II.3, below). The proof of this theorem is similar to that for the corresponding theorem for moments of inertia, given in Appendix I. Note that this theorem is always valid, since areas have, by definition, no thickness. Also, in contrast to the parallel axes theorem, none of the axes need pass through the centroid.

As an example of direct integration, we calculate the second moment of area of a rectangle about its neutral axis:

From the definition:

$$I = \int_A y^2 \, dA$$

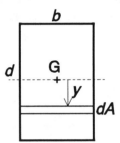

Putting $dA = b \, dy$, this becomes:

$$I = \int_{-\frac{d}{2}}^{\frac{d}{2}} y^2 b \, dy$$

$$= \left[b \frac{y^3}{3} \right]_{-\frac{d}{2}}^{\frac{d}{2}}$$

$$= b \frac{d^3}{12}$$

Notice that the dimensions of second moment of area are [L⁴], and the 'height' appears cubed, with the 'width' appearing to the first power. Virtually all second moments of area have this structure.

We could use the parallel axes theorem to calculate the second moment of area I_B of the rectangle about an axis parallel to the neutral axis, and at the bottom:

$$I_B = I_G + A\left(\frac{d}{2}\right)^2$$

$$= b\frac{d^3}{12} + bd\frac{d^2}{4}$$

$$= b\frac{d^3}{3}$$

Other simple examples, useful for making up more complex shapes are:

- Circle about diameter $\qquad \pi R^4/4$
- Triangle about base $\qquad h^3b/12$
- Triangle about axis through G parallel to base $\qquad h^3b/36$
- Semi-circle about base $\qquad \pi R^4/8$
- Semi-circle about axis through G parallel to base $\qquad \pi R^4\left(\frac{1}{8} - \frac{8}{9}\pi^2\right)$

Other shapes may be obtained by direct integration in the same way. Irregular shapes may need numerical or graphical methods. Complex shapes can be assembled from simpler parts, using the parallel axes theorem.

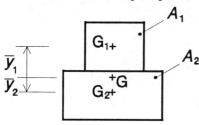

For example, in the figure G is the centroid of the combined shape. The combined second moment of area about G is given by:

$$I_G = I_1 + A_1\bar{y}_1^2$$
$$+ I_2 + A_2\bar{y}_2^2$$

The subscripts 1 and 2 refer to the properties of the two parts *individually*, and I_1 and I_2 are taken about axes through the respective centroids. In the first line, the parallel axes theorem is used to get the second moment of area of the top part about the common centroid. The second line does the same for the bottom part.

II.2.1 Radius of Gyration

Second moment of area is often written in the form $I = Ak^2$. k is the radius of gyration, and may be thought of as a kind of average distance of the area from the axis. For the rectangle, $k^2 = d^2/12$, for the circle it is $R^2/4$, etc. Note that it is the square of radius of gyration which is normally quoted. The parallel axes theorem in terms of radius of gyration becomes:

$$k_{xx}^2 = k_G^2 + \bar{y}^2$$

Extensive tables of second moments of area and/or radii of gyration are given in data and reference books and manufacturers data. These generally give the values about the *principal axes*, which are axes perpendicular to each other, through the centroid. For symmetrical shapes, one or both of them will be axes of symmetry.

II.3 POLAR MOMENTS OF AREA

The polar moments of area are the same as those discussed above, except that the axis concerned is normal to the area, rather than in its plane. By definition, the first polar moment of area about the centroid is zero. The second polar moment of area is defined by:

$$I_{OO} = \int_A r^2 dA$$

where r is the radial distance of the element dA from the axis OO.

The polar moments are evaluated by direct integration (usually in a polar coordinate system) as previously. However, the perpendicular axes theorem (discussed above and in Appendix I, in the context of moments of inertia) is of real utility here, as all areas are laminae. The second polar moment of area is always the sum of the second moments of area about two perpendicular axes in the plane. For example, the second moment of area of a circle about its diameter is $\pi R^4/4$. The second polar moment of area about the centre will be twice this: $\pi R^4/2$. Similarly, the second moment of area of a rectangle about one of its axes of symmetry is $ab^3/12$, and about the other axis is $a^3b/12$. The second polar moment of area about the centroid will be the sum of these: $ab(a^2 + b^2)/12$.

Appendix III

Beam Bending Formulae

Notation:

a		Position of point load from left-hand end
b		$L - a$
c		Position of maximum deflection from right-hand end
E		Young's modulus
I		Second moment of area
L		Beam length
M		Bending moment
s		End slope
W		Point load
w		Uniformly distributed load per unit length
Δ		Maximum deflection

Subscripts:

L		Left-hand end
R		Right-hand end

III.1 CANTILEVER

	s	Δ
	$\dfrac{ML}{EI}$	$\dfrac{ML^2}{2EI}$
	$\dfrac{WL^2}{2EI}$	$\dfrac{WL^3}{3EI}$
	$\dfrac{wL^3}{6EI}$	$\dfrac{wL^4}{8EI}$

III.2 SIMPLY SUPPORTED BEAM

	S	Δ
	$\dfrac{ML}{2EI}$	$\dfrac{ML^2}{8EI}$
	$\dfrac{WL^2}{16EI}$	$\dfrac{WL^3}{48EI}$
	$\dfrac{wL^3}{24EI}$	$\dfrac{5wL^4}{384EI}$
 $(a \leq b) \quad c = \left[\dfrac{b(L+a)}{3}\right]^{0.5}$	$S_R = \dfrac{Wac^2}{2LEI}$ $S_L = \dfrac{L+b}{L+a}S_R$	$\dfrac{Wac^3}{3LEI}$ $a \leq b$

III.3 FIXED ENDS

	M_L, M_R	Δ, c
	$\dfrac{WL}{8}$, $\dfrac{WL}{8}$	$\dfrac{WL^3}{192EI}$, $\dfrac{L}{2}$
	$\dfrac{wL^2}{12}$, $\dfrac{wL^2}{12}$	$\dfrac{wL^4}{384EI}$, $\dfrac{L}{2}$
	$\dfrac{Wab^2}{L^2}$, $\dfrac{Wa^2b}{L^2}$	$\dfrac{Wa^2bc^2}{6EIL^2}$, $\dfrac{2Lb}{L+2b}$
	$\dfrac{3WL}{16}$, 0	$\dfrac{2WL^3}{215EI}$, $0.447L$
	$\dfrac{wL^2}{8}$, 0	$\dfrac{wL^4}{185EI}$, $0.422L$
	$\dfrac{Wab(L+b)}{2L^2}$, 0	$\dfrac{Wa^2bc}{6EIL}$, $L\left[\dfrac{b}{2L+b}\right]^{0.5}$ $b \geq 0.412L$

Appendix IV

Material Properties[*]

The values given in the table overleaf are for guidance only. The actual properties of materials depend on many factors, including the detailed physical composition, ambient conditions (particularly temperature), deformation and temperature history and detailed geometry. These values are for a temperature round about 20°C.

For accurate calculation, it is essential to obtain reliable values for the actual material concerned under the conditions concerned. Such information may be available from suppliers and manufacturers, or may have to be found experimentally.

An indication of the variability to be expected can be obtained by comparing the values given for the same material in various reference books; discrepancies of 100% are not unusual, particularly in non-metals.

Where blanks are left in the table overleaf, this implies either that reliable data are not available, or that values can cover such a wide range that to insert numbers would be misleading.

---

* The data in this Appendix have been obtained from a variety of sources.

Approximate Mechanical Properties of Engineering Materials at 20°C

Material	Density ρ kg/m³	Yield or 0.1% Proof Stress σ_y MN/m²	Ultimate Strength UTS MN/m²	Young's Modulus E GN/m²	Shear Modulus G GN/m²	Bulk Modulus K GN/m²	Poisson's Ratio ν
Aluminium Alloy	2720	30-280	90-300	69	26.5	57.5	0.3
Brass	8450	60-430	330-530	105	38	115	0.35
Cast Iron	7350		280-750	140-200	60	110	0.2-0.3
Concrete	2400	40	43	13.8			0.1
Copper	8960	470-320	200-350	104	46	130	0.35
Glass	2200		8	50-100	26-32	25-50	0.17
Nylon	1150		50-70	2-3	0.7-1.1	3.3-5	0.4
Phenolformaldehyde (Bakelite)	1300		50	7			
Polyvinylchloride (PVC)	1700		28-40	2.5-3.5	0.9-1.25	4.6-6.5	0.41
Polyethylene	960		7-14	0.1-1.25	0.03-0.45	0.17-4.2	0.4-0.45
Polytetrafluorethylene (PTFE)	2200		14-30	0.4-0.7			
Rubber (Natural)	1500		2-10	7-70	2.3-23	v.large	0.5
Steel - Mild	7850	230-460	400-770	207	80	172	0.3
Steel - Stainless	8000	200-580	500-800	213	82	178	0.3
Wood - Soft (Pine)	400-600	30-60	75-125	10-14			
Wood - Hard (Oak)	600-800	50-60	120-150	13			

Appendix III

Index*

A
acceleration, 18
    central, 18
    constant, 47
    gravitational, 27
    variable, 51
action and reaction, 27
amplitude, 58
angle of friction, 78
angular momentum, 104
angular velocity, 101
anisotropic material, 123, 168
annealing, 167
area, centre of *see* centroid
auxiliary equation, 81
axis,
    neutral, 142
    symmetry, 101, 182, 185

B
beam,
    pre-stressed, 149
    simply supported, 37
beam bending formulae, 191-194
bending, 133
    formula, 144

moment, 133
    diagram, 134
    strain, 141
    stress, 141
bending and shear, combined, 145
body force, 33
boundary force, 33
brittle material, 167
buckling, 127
bulk modulus, 124, 196

C
cantilever, 37
centre,
        of area *see* centroid
        of gravity, 34, 181
        of mass, 34, 181
        of volume *see* centroid
        of weight, 181
centrifugal force, 19, 29
centripetal force, 50
centroid, 34, 143, 182, 185
ceramics, 167
characteristic equation, 83
circle, motion in, 49
circumferential stress, 129

---

* This index was compiled using the Macrex software package.

coefficient of friction, 77-78
   table, 78
coefficient of restitution, 95
coil spring, 159
collision,
   perfectly elastic, 95
   perfectly inelastic, 95
column, 37, 127
combinations of loads, 138
complementary function, 62
complementary shear stress, 125
composites, 168
compression testing, 168
concrete, 168
conservation,
   of energy, 71
   of momentum, 91
conservative,
   force, 76
   system, 71
constant,
   acceleration, 47
   excitation, 61
constraints, 19, 34
control surface, 91
Coriolis force, 19, 30
Coulomb friction, 77
couple, 102
creep, 167
critical damping ratio, 82
critically damped oscillation, 82-83

D
d'Alembert force, 29
damped natural frequency, 88
damped resonant frequency, 88
damped vibration,
   forced, 86
   free, 80
damping, 80
   eddy current, 80

fluid, 79
   internal, 80
damping ratio, critical, 82
dashpot, 79
deflection, in bending, 146
deformation, 121
degrees of freedom, 19, 56
density, 196
design of beams, 148
determinacy, static, 39
dimensional analysis, 15
direct stress, 124
dissipative forces, 76
distributed load, 136
dry sliding friction, 77
ductile material, 166
ductile-brittle transition, 167
dynamic friction, 79
dynamics, 14

E
eddy current damping, 80
elastic limit, 166-67
elastic material, 123
elastic modulus *see* Young's modulus
end load and bending, 148
endurance, 177
energy, 71, 92
   conservation, 71
   kinetic, 71, 74
   mechanical, 71
   potential, 71, 74
   strain, 71, 74
epoch, 58
equation of motion, 29, 57, 105
equations, kinematic, 48
equilibrium, 25, 34
   stability of, 34-35
equivalent moment of inertia, 112
excitation, 61
   constant, 61

inertial, 61, 64
    seismic, 61, 65
extension calculation, 126
external forces, 91

F
fail-safe, 172
failure, 171
    definition, 171
failure modes, 173
fatigue, 175
    endurance, 177
    life, 176
    limit, 176
first moment,
    of area, 143, 186
    of mass, 181
flow,
    laminar, 17, 79
    turbulent, 17, 79
fluid friction, 79
force,
    body, 33
    boundary, 33
    centrifugal, 19, 29
    centripetal, 29, 50
    conservative, 76
    Coriolis, 19, 30
    d'Alembert, 29
    dissipative, 76
    electromagnetic, 80
    external, 91
    impulsive, 94
    inertia, 29
    internal, 91
    non-conservative, 76
forced vibration, 55, 61
fracture, 166-67
    brittle, 174
frame of reference, 18
    inertial, 18, 27
    rotating, 18
framework, 40

free body diagram, 19
free vibration, 55
frequency,
    natural, 55
    resonant, 64, 88
    response curve, 63
friction,
    angle of, 78
    coefficient, 77-78
    Coulomb, 77
    dry sliding, 77
    dynamic, 79
    fluid, 76
    force, 77
    limiting, 79
    solid, 76

G
gear ratio, 110
gearing, 109
glass, 167
gravitation, 28
    constant, 28
gravity,
    acceleration due to, 27
    centre of, 34, 181
    effects on oscillations, 60

H
hardness, 169
harmonic motion, simple, 58
hoop stress, 129
    sphere, 129
hydrostatic stress system, 124
hysteresis, 76, 80

I
impulse, 93
impulsive force, 94
inertia force, 29
initial conditions, 58, 82
internal damping, 80
internal force, 91

irreversibility, 76
isotropic material, 123

J
joints, 126
    idealized, 38
    pin, 38

K
kinematic equations, 48
kinematics, 14, 47
kinetic energy, 71, 74, 104-105

L
lag, 58
laminar flow, 17, 79
lead, 58
limiting friction, 79
linear elastic material, 123
load,
    distributed, 136
    external, 36
    idealized, 38
    non-uniformly distributed, 138
    point, 38
    uniformly distributed, 38
logarithmic decrement, 84-85
longitudinal stress, 128
lumped parameters, 57

M
Macaulay's notation, 139
magnification factor, 87
mass, centre of, 34
material properties, 165
    ceramics and glasses, 167
    metals, 165-167
    polymers, 168
    table, 195-196
mechanical energy, 71
mechanics,

Newtonian, 14
    solid, 14
mechanism, 40
members, idealized, 37
microstrain, 122
model,
    mathematical, 15
    physical, 15
modelling, 14
modulus,
    bulk, 124, 196
    elastic *see* Young's modulus
    rigidity, 125
    shear, 125, 196
    Young's, 123, 196
moment,
    bending, 133
    of a force, 25, 102
    of inertia, 104, 106-109, 181-183
        equivalent, 112
    of momentum, 104
moment of area,
    first, 143, 186
    polar, 190
    second, 143, 185-190
momentum, 91
    angular, 104
    conservation, 91
motion,
    equation of, 29, 57, 105
    harmonic, simple, 58

N
natural frequency, 55
    damped, 88
    undamped, 81, 88
negative damping, 82
neutral,
    axis, 142
    plane, 142
Newton's cradle, 96

Newton's Laws, 26
    first, 27
    second, 27, 71, 91
    third, 27, 92
    gravitation, 28
    restitution, 95
nominal stress, 166
non-conservative forces, 76
non-uniform shaft, 160
non-uniformly distributed load, 138
normal stress, 124

O

oscillation,
    critically damped, 82-83
    overdamped, 82
    underdamped, 82-83
oscillator, 55, 80
    linear, 56
    non-linear, 56
overdamped oscillation, 82

P

parallel axes theorem, 108, 183, 187
parameters, lumped, 57
particular integral, 62
perfectly elastic collision, 95
perfectly inelastic collision, 95
permanent set, 166
perpendicular axes theorem, 183, 187-188
phase, 64, 87
    angle, 58
pitch circle diameter, 110
plane, neutral, 142
plastic region, 166
plastics, 168
point load, 38
Poisson's ratio, 123, 196
polar moments of area, 190
polymers, 168
potential energy, 71, 74
power, 75, 111
pre-stressed beam, 149

pressure vessels, 128
proof stress, 167, 196

R

radial stress, 129
radiancy, 58
radius of gyration, 107, 182, 189
ratio,
    critical damping, 82
    gear, 110
    Poisson's, 123, 196
reaction torque, 111
rebound, 94
redundancy, 172
reinforcement, 149
resonance, 64
response, frequency, 63
restitution, coefficient of, 95
rigidity modulus, 125
rotation, 101
    steady, 111
    unsteady, 112
rotation and linear motion, 114
rotational kinetic energy, 104-105

S

S-N curve, 176-177
safety factor, 126, 177
St Venant's principle, 38, 126, 160
second moment,
    of area, 143, 185-190
    of mass see moment of inertia
second polar moment of area, 156,
    158, 190
seismograph, 67
shaft, non-uniform, 160
shear force, 124, 133
    diagram, 134
    relationship to bending moment,
    138
shear modulus, 125, 196
shear strain, 125
shear stress, 124, 128
    in bending, 145
    complementary, 125

distribution, 155
sign conventions, bending, 134
simple harmonic motion, 55, 58
simply supported,
    beam, 135
        distributed load, 137
        point load, 135
    body, 34
solid body rotation, 104
solid friction, 77
solid mechanics, 119
spring stiffness, 51
stability, 159
static determinacy, 39
statics, 14, 33
steady rotation, 111
steady state, 63
    motion, 87
step down gear, 110
step up gear, 110
stiffness, spring, 51
strain, 121-122
    bending, 141
    calculation, 126
    distribution, 142
    energy, 71, 74
    hardening, 166
    volumetric, 124
    yield, 166
stress, 121-122
    bending, 141
    calculation, 126
    circumferential, 129
    concentration, 174
        factor, 174
    direct, 124
    distribution, 122, 126, 142, 149
    hoop, 129
    hydrostatic, 124
    longitudinal, 128
    nominal, 166
    normal, 124
    proof, 167, 196
    radial, 129
    tri-axial, 123
    true, 166
    yield, 166, 196
structure,
    just stiff, 40
    over stiff, 40
    redundant, 39-40
    statically determinate, 39
    statically indeterminate, 39
    under stiff, 40
structures, 36
    joints, 36
    members, 36
strut, 37, 127
superposition, 140
supports,
    built-in, 37
    idealized, 36
    roller, 37
    simple, 37
system, 91

T
tensile test, 165
theory and experiment, 16
tie, 37, 127
torque, 103, 110-112, 155
    diagram, 154
    meter, 157
    reaction, 111
torsion, 154
    shear strain, 154
    tube, 158
torsion formula, 156
torsion shear stress, 154
torsion testing, 169
transient, 63
tri-axial stress, 123

true stress, 166
truss, 40
turbulent flow, 17, 79

U
ultimate tensile strength, 166, 196
undamped natural frequency, 81, 88
underdamped oscillation, 82-83
uniformly distributed load, 38
units,
    dimensions and, 16
    SI, 28
unsteady rotation, 112
UTS *see* ultimate tensile strength

V
variable acceleration, 51
velocity, angular, 101
vibration,
    avoidance, 67
    forced, 55, 61
    free, 55
vibrator, 55
visco-elastic material, 167
viscosity, 79
viscous damper, 79
volume, centre of *see* centroid
volumetric strain, 124

W
weight, centre of, 181
wood, 168
work, 71, 74
work hardening, 167

Y
yield point, 166
yield strain, 166
yield stress, 166, 196
Young's modulus, 123, 196